GABRIELE CATENI

# VOLTERRA
## The Guarnacci
## Etruscan Museum

*Photographs by Fabio Fiaschi*

PACINIeditore

© 2004 by Pacini Editore S.p.A.

ISBN 88-7781-622-8

*Publisher*

Pacini Editore SpA
Via A. Gherardesca
56121 Ospedaletto (Pisa)

*Technical manager*
Mauro Pucciani

*Editor*
Elena Tangheroni Amatori

*Graphic project*
Fabrizio Sodini

*Photolithography and printing*
IGP Industrie Grafiche Pacini

*English translation*
Miriam K. Barbieri

# INDEX

## THE MUSEUM

Mario Guarnacci commemorative medal (1701-1785) – founder of the museum

# INTRODUCTION

The Guarnacci Etruscan Museum, one of Europe's earliest public museums, is worth visiting just to see the impressive "modern" appearance of the elongated shapes in *Ombra della Sera* (Shadow of the Evening) or the disquieting gaze of the old couple portrayed on the *urna degli sposi* (spouses' urn).

The nice building where thousands of Volterra's Etruscan and Roman memorabilia are exhibited, the furnishings of some of its rooms, and the exposition criteria used in some cases are also part of a certain way of making culture.

Thus, the visitors may have the impression of walking through a Museum with two faces and, may we say, with two souls: an ancient one perceived in the rooms with old furniture and many objects often placed one next to the other simply because made of the same material, and a contemporary one reflected in the modern perception of space with few important artifacts accompanied with captions and explanatory panels.

This characteristic is the result of precise choices that kept in view the modalities and the time in which the Institution was founded. They therefore represent a piece of historical evidence as important as the exhibited Etruscan finds and thus should not be forgotten.

From its inception, the Museum has always had the merit of constantly increasing its original collection first through purchases and exchanges, and then by becoming a promoter and protagonist of excavations and researches aimed at a more in-depth understanding of the archeological heritage of the city and its surroundings.

It has in fact become the premises of the historical memory of that ancient Etruscan and Roman town Volterra has been.

The Museum was founded during the middle of the 17th Century, a time marked by intense studies and research on Italian antiquities; a time when Volterra was a true cultural capital.

Mario Guarnacci (1701-1785) was a bizarre personality and an absolute partaker to the stimulating world of 17th-Century Academies. He was responsible for the creation of a permanent antiquities collection in Volterra and was also a very skilled promoter of the city's image in the lively cultural scene of that time. As many other European personalities of his day, the noble abbot from Volterra was also a collector of antiquities, in addition to being an erudite historian. However, he was the first to realize that his purchases did in fact prevent the loss of the many artifacts discovered in Volterra. When he donated the fruits of his decades-long collecting, which had been also financially burdensome, to the "citizens of the town of Volterra", he in fact confirmed the passage of a private patrimony to the community which from that moment on became the true owner.

After numerous events, in 1877 the Museum moved to its present premises in Palazzo Desideri-Tangassi. Niccolò Maffei, director at the time, placed the artifacts according to the most updated contemporary research theories. A valuable example thereof is the arrangement of the over six hundred cinerary urns according to a criteria based on the relief on the lower case of the urn and the placement of other memorabilia according to typology: bronzes, jewelry, glass, ivory, vessels, and so on.

This exhibition criterion went soon out of fashion. Furthermore, there was the need for additional space since the Palazzo hosted the very large Library and the Municipal Historical Archives as well.

Over a century later, the Museum underwent great changes. After the Library and Archives moved to the nearby Palazzo Vigilanti, a more suitable premises for the conservation of their extensive documentary patrimony, the very large third floor was devoted to the exhibition of Hellenistic period artistic crafts. Such a layout required an orderly chronological itinerary, since in Etruscan history the Hellenistic period preluded the Etruscans' assimilation to the Roman Empire.

For this reason, the first floor offers a very synthetic itinerary with an important selection of monuments of Villanovan, Orientalizing, Archaic and Classic periods which then continues on the third floor where, as mentioned previously, the blooming of Etruscan Volterra from the 4th to the 1st Century BC is appropriately exhibited.

This new layout claims to be the basis to the understanding of the old town's historical development and at the same time it makes the various rooms with ancient artifacts more comprehensible.

# THE MUSEUM

First part: from prehistory to the 5<sup>th</sup> Century BC. [Entrance hall-Room I- Room I bis]

## ROOM I

The oldest and most important prehistoric find in Volterra is not exhibited at the Museo Guarnacci but at the Museo Preistorico e Etnografico Pigorini of Rome. It is an **Aeneolithic tomb** inside a grotto found in **Montebradoni**, one of the most suggestive landscapes outside Volterra: the Balze, an immense chasm which through the centuries has swallowed most of one of the town's main Etruscan necropolises. The first showcase displays sketches of the materials found in this tomb and those found in the tombs of Guardistallo and Pomarance dating to the same Aeneolithic period, the Stone and Copper Age between 3,000 and 2,000 BC. These finds are extremely important because they confirm that by the third millennium BC, during the first phase in metal use, the metalliferous hills of the area of Volterra and their mineral resources had already been "discovered".

In the same showcase there are **arrowheads and flint scrapers** of unknown provenance and datable still to the Neolithic and Aeneolithic Ages. The **bronze axes** – winged and with raised edges – belong to a more recent prehistoric period, the Bronze Age between 2,000 and 1,000 BC, and were all found in the area. The handgrip of a winged axe of the early Iron Age has been reconstructed for didactic purposes **(Fig. 1)**.

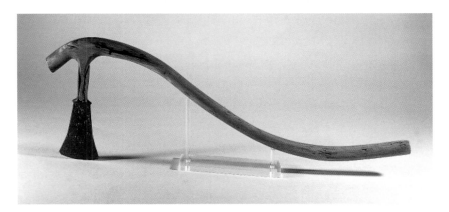

Fig. 1. Reconstruction of hatchet axe handle with wings of the first Iron Age

ROOM I also displays a large number of **Iron Age** artifacts, a period when the town came to life after the union of the dwellings dislocated on the slopes of the hill which were comprised of huts and their burial sites (the necropolises) located in the area of Balze **(necropolis of Badia-Guerruccia)** and **Ripaie**, over which the stadium was later built. Due to the lack of written evidence, this period (between the $10^{th}$ and $8^{th}$ Cent. BC), which may not yet be defined as Etruscan, is conventionally called "Villanovan". In a broad sense, the word defines the most important Italian culture of the early Iron Age characterized by the prevalence of the funeral rite by cremation and by the use of a unique shape of cinerary urn with a bowl lid to collect the remains of the deceased. The name ("Villanovan") comes from a small town near Bologna (Villanova di Castenaso) where the first tomb nucleus of this "culture" was discovered around 1950. Analogously, the word has been used for all those groups (found in Emilia, Tuscany, Marche, Lazio and Campania) that showed similar funeral rites, vessel making, and metal working characteristics.

Burials were individual and characterized by a biconical cinerary urn covered with a bowl and placed in a hole dug in the bare ground, at times with walls covered with stones and closed with a slab. Few bronze objects, usually fibulas (similar to modern-day safety pins, used to fasten a robe) and razors, were part of the burial furnishings. The biconical vases were handmade with black or brown clay without the use of the wheel, polished and decorated with geometrical patterns either incised or painted before firing. The primitive and simple making of the vases was carried out within the family environment, quite different from the production of bronze objects which needed the collaboration of artisans familiar with the complex founding and metal working processes. The burials of this first Villanovan phase point at a society without class distinctions within which wealth was uniformly distributed. The group, comprised of several families bound by kinship ("clan"), must have been the main nucleus of this society based on a rather simple subsistence economy, primarily agriculture, livestock farming and hunting.

ROOM I displays many tombs from the Badia-Guerruccia necropolis (showcases on the left and in the center) excavated with highly scientific criteria at the end of the last century by the famous archeologist Gherardo Ghirardini, and a remarkable selection of artifacts from the necropolis of Ripaie **(Fig. 2-4)**, roughly recuperated in 1969 (showcase on the right). Another important tomb exemplar, reconstructed as it was found in 1969, is

Tomb C (Fig. 5): a hole with stone sides and closed with a sandstone slab. The biconical cinerary urn with a bowl lid was found inside. The burial treasure is composed of only one decorated bow-shaped fibula with disc shaped ribbings (9th Cent. BC).

During the 8th Century, the apparent economic and social homogeny and extreme simplicity of the first phase of the Iron Age morphs into a more articulated distribution of wealth identifiable in the more complex burial furnishings which testify to a series of changes including cultural ones.

Fig. 2. Ripaie Tomb G1

Fig. 3. Ripaie Tomb T

Fig. 4. Biconical bone container

Fig. 5. Ripaie Tomb C

Gradually, the burial techniques became more complex. The first **"ziro" tombs** appear in this phase (mid-8<sup>th</sup> Century BC), represented by a biconical cinerary vase and a rather abundant burial treasure which were placed inside a large terracotta dolium (in Tuscany called "ziro") in turn positioned in a hole dug in the bare ground (exemplars thereof in **ROOM I**, center). In some cases, the "ziro" containing the cinerary of higher social class people was placed inside a real "chamber" made of large stone slabs as in the case of the **tomb of Badia** (Fig. 6) and its extremely rich **burial furnishings** (ENTRANCE HALL).

Fig. 6. Tomb of Badia

Fig. 7. Excavation area inside the Museum

## ROOM I bis

The narrow hallway built during the recent **excavation** (1998-99) for the construction of an elevator offers a close view of a valuable piece of the old town (**Fig. 7**). The stratigraphic intervention brought to light six distinct construction phases identifiable in a rather steep **road** with a N/S orientation built around the 3$^{rd}$ Century BC, and nearby an imposing **wall** of the same period, built parallel to the road, with boss foundations and made of large square blocks. Between the two structures there was a walkway, a sort of beaten earth sidewalk. The stone and pebble road is the only visible trace of Volterra's earliest road system, also used during Roman time until the 1$^{st}$ Century AD when it was abandoned. The large wall, which is part of the building (NW/SE orientation) at the end of the excavation site, belongs to the last and more recent construction phases: indeed, it cuts through both the road and the parallel wall. During the late Roman period this structure was reused as a small ditch or sewer.

Let us now take a closer look at the large showcase on the right displaying the bronze burial furnishings of the **tomb of the warrior** discovered in 1996 on top of **Poggio alle Croci**, a hillock close to town which owes its macabre name

Fig. 8. Crested helmet
(Tomb of the Warrior)

Fig. 9. Double flask
(Tomb of the Warrior)

(roughly, the Hill of the Crosses) to the Medieval practice of raising on this site the blocks and gallows for those sentenced to death.

The remarkable **crested helmet (Fig. 8)** with extremely fine embossed geometric decorations typical of the Villanovan period is a prestigious evidence of the prince-warrior's power who was buried with his weapons (**sword, large lance, javelin**), two horse **bits** that belonged to a pair of horses which drew his war chariot, and objects used in banquets like the **cup** and the splendid laminated **double flask (Fig. 9)** with embossed decorations, unique in its type. The burial furnishings are datable back to the last decades of the 8$^{th}$ Century BC, the same dating attributed to the other tomb exhibited in the showcase on the back wall which was discovered during the 19$^{th}$-Century excavations at Badia: the so-called **Manetti tomb (Fig. 10)**.

Fig. 10. Manetti Tomb from Montebradoni

Fig. 11. Tomb U1 of Ripaie

The following period is generally called **"Orientalizing"** (end 8th-7th Cent. BC) and is characterized by a massif flow of Oriental exotic (Syria, Phoenicia and Egypt) and Greek objects into Etruria and their consequent local imitation. This period, however, is not well documented by the tombs found in and around Volterra as they are completely made without the use of those important materials commonly found in the necropolises of northern Etruria and other coastal areas. The Orientalizing period was mostly a trading phenomenon which influenced those centers in direct contact with Oriental and Greek merchants. A prestigious burial example of the first Orientalizing period is **U1 tomb of Ripaie** (reconstructed in the center of **ROOM I**) (**Fig. 11**).

This **ziro** tomb is an emblematic example of the first Orientalizing period emphasized by the richness of bronze and iron artifacts **(weapons, ornamental objects, drinking cup)** and the total absence of imported materials. Once again, Volterra's geographic location hindered direct trade exchanges with Greek and Oriental merchants, contrary to the long-lasting and extended exchanges that took place in Populonia. Most likely trade exchanges were attracted to this town, the only Etruscan center built on the seaside, and consequently Populonia became Volterra's intermediary during the second half of the 8th Century BC.

**Q1 tomb of Ripaie (ENTRANCE HALL) (Fig. 12)** clearly demonstrates how these Oriental and Greek influences interfered with a substantially static culture and society still based on the past. In fact, the new elements are the **Etruscan-Corinthian** (local imitations of small vessels made in Corinth, Greece) **aryballos** (scent or oil vase) produced in southern Etrurian shops, and the **bronze belt plaques** which definitely reveal an oriental taste and style. However, the tomb architecture (which also imitates large constructions with a pseudo-cupola cover) and the type of ziro burial still reflect typical Villanovan tradition.

Fig. 12. Tomb Q1 of Ripaie

Fig. 13. Kyathos
from Monteriggioni

## ROOM II

Showcase 1

Kyathos (ladle or drinking cup) from Monteriggioni (Siena) (Fig. 13). It comes from a small despoliated chamber tomb excavated in 1898 (Terrosi collection).

This cup is made of a not well depurated bucchero mixture with decorated external part of the handle and inside of the cup. The base reveals an Etruscan inscription carved prior to firing: *mini muluvanice vhlakunaie venel* (I was donated by venel flakunaie). The type of mixture and the inscription's paleographic characters link this cup to a southern-Etruscan production area, perhaps near Populonia. The formula used in the inscription is particularly interesting since it bears both the personal name (*venel*) and the aristocratic name (*vhlakunaie*) to indicate the person who donated this prestigious gift (*mini muluvanice* = I was donated) during a particular ceremony (mid-7th Cent. BC).

Archaic bronze statuettes (second half of 7th-early 6th Cent. BC). From left to right: no. 134, 145 figures of bovidae, no. 7 male bronze statuette in standing position with legs together and the left hand on his hip. The right hand extends in front and it used to hold an object, most likely a lance.

He has a conic hat (*tutulus*) and wears only a loincloth strongly raised in correspondence to the genitals; no. **24, 20/1, 21/1** variations of the same type of male bronze statuette: they are in standing position with their arms detached from the body and extending in front. They wear a loincloth resembling shorts with engraved rims. They originally held a sword. The place of origin of two exemplars is known: n. **20/1** comes from Colloreto near Volterra, and **21/1** from the town's acropolis. The latter was discovered during the first excavations carried out by Doro Levi in 1926 (**Fig. 14**).

Fig. 14. Male bronze statuette

no. **1929/13-5 female statuette of an offerer.** She held in her hand an object, now lost, most likely a vase to draw water (**Fig. 17**).

no. **1/55b: female bronze statuette.** Her arms rest along the body and she holds in her hands two long braids that fall over her breasts. A typical gesture of funeral mourning (**Fig. 16**).

no. **65: female bronze statuette** in standing position with her arms extending in front. She holds an apple in her right hand. The body has a flattened laminated shape, the head is covered by a robe that rests on her shoulders. The long braids, executed with thin carved lines fall on her shoulders. No. **5/52b:** female bronze statuette in standing position with legs together. The arms rest along the body, which is proportionately too short with respect to the head. She wears a chiton and a robe that covers her head. Compared to the first three exemplars dating back to the second half of the 7th Century BC, the latter is slightly younger (beginning 6th Cent. BC).

Fig. 15. Warrior bronze statuette no. 24

Fig. 16. Female bronze statuette no. 1/55b

Fig. 17. Female bronze statuette

Showcase 2
**Jewelry from Gesseri** (Volterra) **(Fig. 18).** Donated by Bishop G. Incontri in 1839. They come from a chamber tomb casually discovered at the be-ginning of the last century in the for-est of Berignone, about 15 km from Volterra, which was part of the bish-op's revenue. In the middle: chain with large pin perhaps used as head-gear; to the sides: four leech fibulas dug out on the inside, a "dragon" fibu-la with antennae and two fragments, perhaps belonging to another winding bow-shaped fibula. These objects, which increase the Orientalizing con-text of the territory of Volterra, are typologically linked to princely tomb

furnishings of northern Etruria such as those in Populonia and Vetulonia. It is possible that the objects come from Vetulonia (650-625 BC).

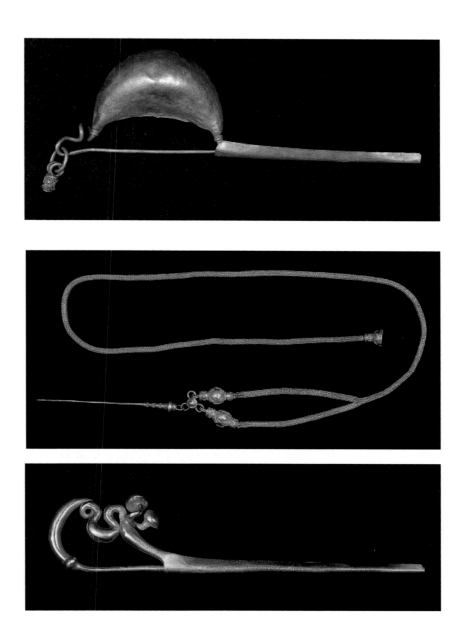

Fig. 18. Jewelry from Gesseri

**Funeral stele fragment from Badia**

Discovered in 1860 at the foot of the Balze chasm. There is only the lower part of the monument with the legs of two male figures in bas-relief standing in front of each other and separated by a tree. On the left side, the Etruscan inscription *mi leasies* [I (am) from Leasie].

**Funeral stele of the warrior AVILE TITE (Fig. 19)**

The monument is made of a squared elongated rectangular shape slab arched at the top and a relief edge with a flat fillet on the left side on which there is a deep Etruscan engraving (from below upwards and from right to left: *mi aviles tite[s...] uxsie mulenike.* [I (belong) to Avile Tite (…)chsie donated me]. The right side completely lacks the relief edge, traces of which are found on the lower corner: the lower part of the stele was cut to adapt its size to a particular placement. In the center of the stele, a standing virile relief figure in profile slightly moving to the left and holding a lance in his right hand extended in front. The left arm is bent at an obtuse angle and rests on his hip; the hand (almost completely lost) is resting on a sword-knife with bird-head handle hanging sideways on the belt. The man has a beard and long wavy hair in horizontal layers.

One legitimately believes the figure wore a tunic (as suggested by the marks on the neck and left arm) with over a **lorica** (cuirass) and had painted details for the shoulder plates. This sculpture belongs to the northern area series of single-figure Etruscan steles widespread in Tyrrhenian Etruria and the Florentine countryside. From a stylistic point of view, it echoes Greek-Oriental patterns. Around 560 BC.

Fig. 19. Funerary stele of Avile Tite

# ROOM III

*Showcase 1 (center of the room)*
**Marble head** (perhaps **Apollo**) also known as "Lorenzini Head" **(Fig. 20).**
This extraordinary monument of late-Archaic Etruscan sculpture is at the center of a legal dispute pertaining its ownership. Due to this issue, the exhibited monument is simply a reproduction. The original is preserved in the Museum's storage rooms.
The head is larger than normal size and most likely belonged to the statue of a divinity, perhaps Apollo. If this were the case, the exemplar would be the earliest known marble statue of Central Etruria.

Fig. 20. "Lorenzini Head"

Even though some still believe it is a Greek original, it is commonly accepted it was executed by an Etruscan. This fact is based on details such as the massive compaction of the face, the unique and complex hairstyle and the rendering of the eyebrows in relief. The latter detail is not found in any other Greek marble work of that time, yet it is rather common in Etruscan bronze statues produced in the northern Tyrrhenian area and in hinterland Etruria up to Marzabotto. The marble head from Volterra is acknowledged as being their true father. The derivation from a bronze model is clearly evident in the execution of the eyes which had to be filled with a glass and bone mixture, as in the case of large bronze statues **(480-460 BC).**

*Showcase 2 (on the right)*
This showcase and the one in front display artifacts datable to the 5th Century BC, a not very well-documented period in Volterra compared to other large Etrurian cities. For this reason, the artifacts are extremely important to the reconstruction of the town's historical development. Down below, fragments of an **Attic amphora with black figures** coming from the necropolis of Badia (530-510 BC). On top: large **cinerary vase** from Villamagna with armed-soldier stamp decorations, similar to the stele of Avile Tite. Next (to the left), an **Attic krater (Fig. 22)** from Montebradoni with figures of warriors attributed to a pottery decorator close to **Pittore di Altamura** (470 BC). Down below: **terracotta slab** (sima recta) with a figure of a knight coming from the Acropolis (first half of the 5th Cent. BC). Next: horseshoe-shaped stele with Etruscan inscription *mi ma larisa hevinas* from Torricchi (necropolis of Ulimeto). On top: two **column kraters** attributed to Pittore dello stamnos 824 (4th Cent. BC).

*Showcase 3 (on the left)*
On the higher shelf, a series of **bronze statuettes** of the **5th Century BC**. They are small figures executed with full casting portraying male figures of offerers (MG 2069, 2175) as well as female ones (MG 2077, 2080, 2078) **(Fig. 21)** and intended as votive offerings in the sanctuaries. The large size **warrior head** (MG 2104) similar to the one of the famous suicidal Aiace from Populonia is worth mentioning.

Fig. 22. Attic krater from Montebradoni

Fig. 21. Female bronze statuette

Fig. 23. "Box-shaped" gold earrings

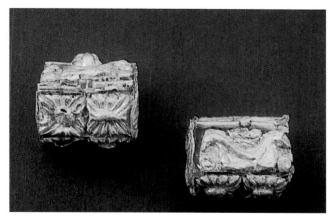

The lower shelf displays a plain **mirror** with a tang, a spike to be inserted into a separate handle (ivory or bone), which was found in **tomb III of the necropolis of Guerruccia**; next, **"box" earrings (Fig. 23)** with an embossed decoration typical of 5ᵗʰ-Century BC jewelry. Under the magnifying glass, a scarab in cornelian (Fig. 24) with an engraved dog figure scratching its snout coming from the same tomb III of Guerruccia; another **scarab with warrior figure and Greek inscription (*LYSANDROS*)**, most likely the engraver's name.

This jewelry, once part of the original Mario Guarnacci collection, was found in Volterra in the 1750s. On the far right of the showcase, a **mirror carved** with a pair of female dancers, one of Etruscan carving masterpieces dated 480 BC.

Fig. 24. Scarab no. 147 with warrior figure

ROOMS III-IX and the whole **second floor** of the Museum host what is now restrictively known as the **"Guarnacci collection"**. In truth, the noble abbot's original collection is only a part of the Museum's patrimony, which has increased year after year owing to excavations, donations, and purchases.

The layout of the "historical nucleus" was codified as we see it today by Niccolò Maffei in 1877. When beginning the tour, it is necessary to bear in mind the following. First of all, the **cinerary urns** that comprise the largest and most representative nucleus of the collection are grouped together according to the **theme of the bas-relief incised on the lower case of the urn**, an en vogue philological criterion at the end of the last century. Second, due to the rather unscientific excavation methods adopted in the 1700s and 1800s, in most cases the lid placed on top of the urn is not the original one.

The core nucleus of the exhibit is based on the over **600 cinerary urn** exemplars (**ROOMS III** to **IX** and **XIII-XIV-XVI-XIX**). From the first discoveries, the typical local Hellenistic products ($3^{rd}$-$1^{st}$ Cent. BC) have fomented the interest of the scientific world in the complex and stimulating historical, artistic, and social problematic linked to the dynamics of their production.

The urns of Volterra and its territory appear like small sarcophagi made of two elements: the lid and the ash container (urn). The two main urn types are a combination of these elements: a case with double sloping cover or a human figure.

The first type is chronologically antecedent and is made of a parallelepiped case not sculpted but decorated with geometrical or floral patterns with a range of bright colors (as visible in the better preserved exemplars) and with a double sloping cover with central beam and accentuated oblique joists, at times with decorative elements.

A wealth of examples of this first urn production phase ($5^{th}$-$4^{th}$ Cent.) is visible in **ROOM III** (right wall). The first exemplars of parallelepiped urn cases (the earlier ones do not display any carving) with the lid shaped as a human figure recumbent on a side as though at a banquet date back to the beginning of the $3^{rd}$ Century BC and follow a pattern which will remain unaltered throughout their entire production time. They were probably the result of a true religious "revolution", or at least of a strong change in the funeral rite concept, the reasons of which are unknown.

Even though the immediate feeling when walking through the Museum is that of discovering the somatic traits of the ancient Etruscans of the area of Volterra, this is true only for the later phases of urn production. In the earlier phase, it was more a generic representation of faces rather than a true portrait. Only at the beginning of the 1$^{st}$ Century BC, the veristic style was developed and confirmed under the influence of contemporary urban portrait. Between these two extremely opposed styles, there is a complex articulation of different types of representation linked to the various relationship levels with Greek-Hellenistic and Middle-Italic idealized models.

The figurative representation of the cases presents yet another unique problem: the typical example with a continuous bas-relief decoration placed between the upper cornice and the lower base begins in late 2$^{nd}$ Century and may be defined as 'local' with scenes linked to daily life [ROOMS III-IX, ground floor], and as "erudite" when Greek mythological models are featured [ROOMS XIII-XIX, second floor].

It appears there were two clientele levels: the middle class of artisans and small land owners linked to ancient beliefs, and the aristocratic one which required refined products echoing Greek models to express their social status.

## ROOM III

*Right wall*

Simple urns: no. 16, 517, 518, 491, 459, 582, 519, 581, 445, 456, 520, 531, 530, 60, 10, 53, 584, 51, 412, 63.

Urns no. 531, 530 reveal clear traces of the original polychromy, no. 53 has bas-relief decorations on three sides. The decorative elements of the tympanum of no. 584 are the hands.

*Left wall*

1) Urns with floral decorations, rosette between acanthus leaves or alone: no. 146, 29, 476, 26, 30, 391, 537, 36, 539, 562, 38, 563, 536.

2) Urns with flower spirals: no. 443, 556, 578.

Inside the showcase: urn no. 538: on the case, central rosette surrounded by rosette ornaments. This is an extraordinary document of tufa production dating mid-2$^{nd}$ Century BC. (**Fig. 25**).

Back wall on the left: no. 124 (**Fig. 26**) sarcophagus from the hypogeum of Flave; male figure on the lid, procession of magistrates on the case.

Back wall on the right: no. 123 sarcophagus from the hypogeum of Flave; female figure on the lid, farewell scene on the case.

These sarcophagi are the only examples of this type of monument in Volterra and reflect a funerary rite still strongly linked to cremation. They come from a hypogeum excavated in the necropolis of Portone in 1760. A total of forty cinerary urns come from the same tomb.

Fig. 25. Female portrait no. 538

Fig. 26. Sarcophagus of Laris Flave

## ROOM IV

*Demons, masks and symbols*

*Left wall* coming from ROOM III
Winged demons holding a rosette:
no. **32, 33.**
Winged demons holding an umbilicated patera: no. **298, 162, 34.**
Crossed vegetation knots: no. **533,
534, 535.** Medusa head: no. **38** (Fig.
**27**). Medusa head and tragic masks between capitals: no. **42, 43, 40.**
*Back wall*
Upper shelf: late urns with parallelepiped case and truncated pyrami-
dal lid.
Birds pecking a plant: no. **555,
532, 635.**

Fig. 27. Urn no. 38

Terracotta double sloping urns with applied male or lion head relieves: no. 12, 387.

Terracotta urns with a recumbent male on the lid and winged female figures decorated on the edges.

*Right wall*

no. 438: winged female demon portrayed on the case, floral decorations on the sides and recumbent male on the lid (alabaster).

no. 37: Medusa head on the case, half-closed window on the side, a lozenge-decorated balustrade above.

*Lower shelf*

no. 600: made of tufa with applied terracotta decorations, Medusa heads in the center with knotted serpents. Above, only two of the four original terracotta lion heads are visible. Medusa heads on the sides, identical to the ones in front.

no. 31: rosette with pistil flanked by dolphins.

no. 39: made of tufa. Acanthus leaves on the case that rise symmetrically from the base on both sides of the Medusa head; the latter has two small wings bent on the temples, the heads of the two serpents knotted on the head extend beyond the wings, two rosettes on the higher edges.

Under urn no. 39: memorial stone on the floor.

no. 378: floral motifs on the case.

no. 54: made of tufa, half-laying recumbent figure with patera. On the case, bas-relief imitating the sides of a kline with footrest with two doves resting on top; on the side, a male figure extends his hand to Charon. Above: four alabaster case fragments with winged demons.


# ROOM V

*Wild and imaginary animals*

The urns exhibited in this room portray real or imaginary animals, either alone or fighting, according to the following order: urns with animals or marine creatures (no. 44, 49, 57, 58, 61, 62, 64, 66, 67, 70, 73, 383, 541, 564); urns with fighting scenes with marine creatures (no. 71, 449); urns with griffons (no. 47, 48, 50, 363, 404, 490, 577); fighting scenes with griffons.

no. **44:** female figure on the lid with fan and pomegranate. Marine dragon on the case (Ketos).

no. **57:** female figure on the lid. On the case a demon holds the reins of four horses coming out from the waves. The waves are highly stylized in curls and among them two flitting dolphins. On the sides, representation of a double door **(Fig. 28)**.

Fig. 28. Urn case no. 57

Fig. 29. Lid no. 64

no. **58, 61, 62, 64** (Fig. 29), **66, 67, 70, 73, 383, 541, 564, 71, 449**: various representations of full-faced winged marine demon, with a human upper body and a serpent lower part (Scylla?).

no. **47, 48, 50, 363, 404, 490, 577**: representation of rampant female griffons.

Between the animals there is an amphora (**47, 48, 363, 404**), a tree (**50, 577**), a demon (**490**).

no. **120**: on the case, representation of a griffon fighting an Amazon. Two figures are portrayed on the left side of the urn, the female one is standing wielding a long lance, the other one is sitting. On the other side, a sitting man and a standing woman shake hands in greeting.

no. **352, 416, 432, 540**: fight between the Arimaspi and winged female griffon.

no. **5**: on the lid, reclining female figure. On the case, two felines attack an animal.

Urn case no. **52**: a winged griffon attacks a deer. This case is of doubtful authenticity.

no. **589**: double sloping cover, two rampant birds with a floral element in the center. On the case, a winged griffon attacks a deer.

no. **349**: wild boar hunting scene with winged heroes. Rosette with four-petal corolla on the sides.

**ROOMS VI, VII, VIII and IX** host those urns with bas-reliefs linked to the **journey of the deceased to the afterlife**, a very successful theme among the Etruscans of the area of Volterra. It is a typical local repertoire without erudite models and its predominant characteristic is the sketchiness of the execution: the figures lack spatial depth, are portrayed frontally, are monotonous and lack movement. Typical examples are the relieves portraying the moment right before the journey begins: the **farewell of the deceased from his family (ROOM VI)** when the loving handshake takes place, the "dextrarum iunctio", signaling the bond of love between the living and deceased members of a family.

According to the Etruscan beliefs, the journey to the afterlife curiously takes place **on a horse (ROOM VII)** or **on a chariot (ROOM VIII)**: thus, it was believed there were roads or paths leading to the world of the dead, unlike in Greece where it was located beyond the sea.

The deceased, wearing a robe and riding a horse, was accompanied by a servant (viator) with a provision sack on his shoulder. In the underworld, he is greeted by a monstrous, threatening demon with a beard, pointy ears, hooked nose, at times with wings, and usually wielding a large hammer. It is **Charun**, the Etruscan Charon: the true personification of death.

The **theme of the journey** appears to be widely used in earliest urn productions with bas-relief figures (end 3$^{rd}$ Cent.) and then revived later on (1$^{st}$ Cent. BC-1$^{st}$ Cent. AD) in the scenes of trips on a **chariot (ROOM VIII)**, a sort of covered wagon most likely of Celtic origin inside which lay the deceased or the married couple, also joined in death.

Special types of trips are represented with **official processions (ROOM VI** - urns **153, 157, 154, 1255; ROOM IX** - urns **166, 167, 184, 161, 165, 168, 169, 170, 171, 483, 487)**. In this case, the celebrative function of the deceased's role in society is clearly evident.


ROOM VI

*Scenes of funerary farewell*


no. **75, 76,77, 78, 79, 82, 83, 84, 85, 86, 87, 267, 301, 360, 405, 408, 473, 544, 546, 547, 548, 566, 567, 568, 569.** Scenes of funerary farewell: the wife and husband are depicted in the "dextrarum iunctio" moment: they shake hands to say goodbye. It is not clear whom of the two is about to begin the journey to the afterlife. Urn no. **78** bears an inscription on the lid: *a. trepi. ril. LXV* ("aule trepi, 65 years of age").

no. **74, 81, 89, 543.** Farewell scenes of the deceased on a kline (bed).

no. **129, 565.** Farewell scene in front of a tomb.

no. **153, 157, 154** (case only), **155.** Scenes of a magistrate procession. Most likely the deceased covered an important public position and is thus accompanied to the afterlife by a procession according to his social position: insignias of power (fasces), a music band (no. **157**), the symbols of the magistracy (the rotuli and the curule chair, no. **154, 155**).

# ROOM VII

*Journey to the underworld*

no. 90, 91, 92, 93, 94, 95, 96, 97, 98, 99, 122 (Fig. 30), 156, 365, 570, 571, 572, 586, 104. Farewell scene of the deceased on horse before he begins his journey to the afterlife.

no. 107, 110, 111, 112, 113, 115, 116, 117, 118, 125, 126, 397, 414, 417, 549, 574, 576. Scene of the departure of the deceased on horse, with farewell from his family.

no. 100 (Fig. 33), 101, 102, 103, 105, 106 (case), 109, 114, 121 (case) (Fig. 34), 127, 424, 602. Scene of the journey to the afterlife on horse with demons (Fig. 32).

no. 128, 287, 451, 57. Miscellaneous scenes of the journey on horse.

Fig. 30. Urn case no. 122

Fig. 31. Urn no. 156

Fig. 32. Urn case no. 118

Fig. 33. Urn no. 100

Fig. 34. Urn case no. 121

34

Fig. 35. Urn lid no. 114

## ROOM VIII

*Journey to the underworld on a chariot*

no. 132, 133, 134, 135, 136, 137, 138, 139, 140, 141, 142, 143, 144, 145, 148, 149, 150, 151, 452, 463, 481, 485, 486, 551 (lid),

Fig. 36. Urn lid no. 136

552, 711 (Fig. 38), 722, 611 (terracotta lid). All these urns depict the theme of the journey on a chariot, a covered two-wheeled wagon drawn by a pair of mules or horses. Inside the chariot, the deceased or married couple, together also for the last trip. The theme is also widely used in a later production period (1$^{st}$ Cent.). Noteworthy is lid no. 136 which represents

Fig. 37. Alabaster urn no. 141

the **haruspex** *aule lecu*, son of Laris, who died at thirty five. The priest is portrayed as he is foretelling the future from the goat liver he holds in his left hand (**Fig. 36**).

Fig. 38. Alabaster urn no. 711

# ROOM IX

*Journey to the underworld on a quadriga, by sea, and miscellaneous subjects*

no. 160, 161, 165, 168, 169, 171, 173, 364, 482, 483, 487. *A magistrate's journey to the underworld on a quadriga.*
no. 181, 166, 167. *A warrior's journey to the underworld on a quadriga.* In two cases (166, 167) the man in accompanied by a veiled woman, perhaps his wife.
no. 276, 277. *Journey to the underworld by sea.*
no. 591. *Sheep herding scene.*
no. 172, 182, 183, 379, 400. *The rape of Proserpina* (Fig. 39).
no. 130, 559. *Funerary games in honor of the deceased.*
n. 621. *Scene of unknown meaning,* perhaps the deceased in the reign of the Blessed.
Miscellaneous representations: no. 575, *aggression,* no. 425, 500 *homicide;* no. 131 *scene at a school;* no. 212 *sacrifice of a pig.*

The colossal **statue of abbot Guarnacci** executed by sculptor P. Bagnolesi (1867) is located on the stairs that lead to the second floor.
There are also many **Latin epigraphs** on the walls of the stairs that join the ground floor to the second floor. Some of them come from either Volterra or its countryside (as indicated by each caption), others were purchased by Guarnacci during his sojourn at the diocesan curia in Rome during the papacy of Benedict XIII, Clement XII and Benedict XIV.

Fig. 39. Urn case no. 400

# FIRST FLOOR

Since 1877, **ROOM III** and the entire left wing of the palace (**ROOMS XIV-XIX**) were devoted to the exhibition of a very rich – and extremely monotonous – collection of cinerary urns portraying episodes from **Greek mythology**.

It is believed that for the creation of their sculptures, the sculptors of the Volterra area used models that reproduced famous works of art dealing with mythology, paintings in particular. Therefore, these themes in some way testify that important families of Etruscan Volterra such as the Ceicna, Ati, Luvisu, Cneuna and others which names are found on the epitaphs, were strongly interested in such subjects and enjoyed having events well known to them represented on their funerary monument. Presumably, Hellenistic culture arrived in Volterra through master artisans working for wealthy Etruscan families, some of whom most likely came directly from Greece.

These master artisans were able to set up sculpting schools and, based on their example and their works, trained local second-rate sculptors. In conclusion Volterra's urns, which were linked to a private and funerary context, offer the widest and most complete panorama on Hellenic artistic culture in Etruria. In addition, they depict the social and economic reality of this big Etruscan city and, in some way, the funerary ideology of important local families and of the many less wealthy families that followed their example.

In concomitance to the new orientations of research and exhibition criteria this large space, previously less visited, has recently been devoted to the exhibit of **themes and masterpieces of Hellenistic Volterra (4$^{th}$-1$^{st}$ Century BC)**. This space has now become part of the new Museum itinerary.

To such end, some urns have been "sacrificed" (placed in containers that may be opened upon request by researchers) to make room for some themes capable of offering an immediate representation of the world of Etruscan artisanship. The mythological theme is represented here by the very famous story of Ulysses (**ROOM XIV**) and **ROOM XVI** displays the most beautiful alabaster urns that were part of the original itinerary, one urn for each type of scene represented.

## ROOM XIII

In the center of the room, a mosaic floor discovered in 1884 coming from the Terme of S. Felice. On the right, relief model of the Terme of S. Felice. From the right wall entering the room: *Minotaur saga.* 1) no. **355**: *the construction of the wooden cow by hand of Dedalo* (Fig. 40).
2) no. **299**: *birth of the small Minotaur* (Fig. 41); no. **288, 434, 435**: *Arianna intercedes to calm Minos' rage.*
3) no. **264, 300**: *Theseus kills the Minotaur.*
*Scenes of uncertain meaning*: no. **199, 496** (fragments): *homicide in a sacred place*; no. **262**: *fighting of two men*; no. **147, 211, 213**: *fighting in front of a small temple*; no. **502**: *fighting warrior*; no. **339**: *unidentified scene*; no. **208, 209, 210, 214, 394, 395**: *two prisoners are about to be sacrificed* and two female priests pour holy water on their heads. Recently, this episode has been linked to *Chryses*, the tragedy of Pacuvio and of which some fragments are preserved. In this case, the two tied figures would be Orestes and Pylades.
no. **201, 206, 207, 489** (fragments): Scene depicting a *drawing*. It is perhaps the consultation of an oracle: from a large krater the priest takes out a small slab (*sors*) on which the oracle's response is written. This *sortilegium* scene is perhaps linked to the previously mentioned prisoner episode. Noteworthy is

Fig. 40. Urn no. 355

Fig. 41. Urn case no. 299

Fig. 42. Urn lid no. 262

the fact that the shape of the small slab corresponds to real bronze *sortes* found in Etruria (**Fig. 43**).

no. **191, 192, 193, 194, 195, 196, 484, 494**: *banqueting scene*. Perhaps it is one instance of Euripides' *Melanippe* tragedy.

no. **158, 159, 164, 174, 189, 442, 455**: *scene with warriors on a quadriga*.

no. **497**: terracotta urn with pertinent lid representing *Medea escaping from Corinth*, found in 1873 during Cinci's excavations in the necropolis of Portone. No. **175, 176, 177, 178, 179, 180, 187, 439, 471, 472, 593-597** (fragments): *Pelope and Ippodamia's return from the fatal run* (**Fig. 44**). Other relieves on the story of Pelope and Ippodamia are exhibited in **ROOM XVI** (urns **181, 260, 261, 362, 450, 506, 592**: *killing of Enomao* by hand of Pelope) and **XIX** (urns **4, 215, 216, 217, 218, 219, 220, 221, 222, 381, 418, 419, 433, 515, 603**: *killing of Mirtilo*, Enomao's charioteer) (**Fig. 45**).

Urn **351**: *monster rising from the puteal*. This Etruscan legend still exists today. When narrating the behavior of lightning, the historian and naturalist Pliny the Elder recalls an ancient Etruscan story according to which King Porsenna evoked a lightning bolt to kill a monster the Etruscans called Olta, which was threatening the town of Volsinii. In the bas-relieves of no. **351** and **350** (**ROOM XXXI, third floor**) a monstrous animal with a wolf head is forced into a well. The edge of the latter is similar to Roman-age *puteals*, built to delimitate the areas hit by lightning: they were the lightnings' "tomb".

Fig. 43. Urn case no. 201

Fig. 44. Urn case no. 178

Fig. 45. Urn case no. 217

## ROOM XIV

In the center, urns regarding the myth of Ulysses, one of the most famous and most appreciated heroes of Greek mythology, also found in many of Volterra's urn bas-relieves.

In the Iliad, in which the vision of strength, beauty, wealth, and power of Greek warrior aristocracy of the 8th Century BC is emphasized, the figure of Odysseus/Ulysses has a secondary role. On the contrary, he is the unquestionable protagonist of the Odyssey, a work linked to a more human and totally different world.

Even though in the poem of the Iliad Ulysses does not shine with distinct physical qualities, he is as brave a warrior as many others and stands out for some unique characteristics: his intelligence and his speechmaking skills that qualify him as mediator and diplomat in specific instances; in addition, his shrewdness (for example, the decisive invention of the wooden horse that will lead to the destruction of Troy) and his ability to find stratagems to overcome difficult situations.

With respect to traditional values, he is thus an atypical hero and in the Odyssey he takes on the role of a very clever and patient person. Compared to the Iliad, the setting of this poem is completely different: not only within the aristocratic circle of heroes, but also that of the common people, even the most humble ones such as the swineherd or the beggar. In this context and with his human and moral characteristics, Ulysses is perceived as the ideal of a new kind of man: he utilizes his intelligence in all adventurous circumstances he encounters, his shrewdness helps him when he is in difficulty, his speechmaking skills fascinate all his interlocutors.

Due to his curiosity, his desire to learn and to discover, which leads him to distant lands, Homer's Ulysses may be considered as the prototype of the European man. The hero further tests himself experimenting and defying the forces of nature. Odysseus/Ulysses' capacity to feel pain makes him a profound human character: suffering is a specific trait of this homesick survivor who returns to his homeland and to his dear after many adventures.

The exciting experiences of this character were widely acknowledged and appreciated in Volterra where many cinerary urns depict episodes linked to Ulysses' saga; in particular, the incident of the Mermaids is frequently represented.

ENTERING on the LEFT: urn case no. 283 (*Ulysses and the Mermaids*); on the RIGHT: case no. 462 (*Ulysses and the Mermaids*: Odyssey IX, vv. 414) ON THE BACK WALL from left to right: urn case no. 428: *Ulysses kills the Suitors* (Proci); no. 336: *Circe turns Ulysses' companions into animals*; no. 232: *Ulysses meets Filottete on the island of Lemno*; no. 268: *Blinding of Polyphemus* (Fig. 46); no. 278: *Ulysses and the Mermaids* (Fig. 47).

Fig. 46. Urn case no. 268

Fig. 47. Urn case no. 278

In the center of the room, one of the most important and famous monuments of the Museum of Volterra: the elongated bronze statue better known as "**Ombra della Sera**" (Shadow of the Evening) (**Fig. 48**). This evocative definition, improperly attributed to Gabriele D'Annunzio, well suits this unique elongated bronze which plaster of the human figure evokes the image of the shadow projected on the ground at sunset. There is no certain information concerning when and where it was found. Anton Francesco Gori, an 1800s Florentine intellectual, saw this bronze at the small **Buonarroti collection** in Florence and published a drawing of the statuette in his work Museum Etruscum (**1737**), claiming it came from Volterra.

Due to his relations with Florentine antique dealers, after 1750 Mario Guarnacci got a hold of the bronze statuette either purchasing it or by exchange, and included it in his collection. Even though this scarce information does not allow a historical and archeological reconstruction, it is unequivocal and thus permits the elimination of those false and imaginary legends on the finding of this bronze as well as the halo of mystery

Fig. 48. Ombra della sera (Shadow of the Evening)

Ombra della sera
(Shadow of the Evening) (details)

emanated by its singularity. This statuette was surely found in Volterra before 1737. Notwithstanding the uniqueness of its execution and dimensions, the bronze is not an isolated piece but belongs to the category of elongated votive offerings portraying haruspexes, offerers, and deities well-documented in central Italy and in particular in hinterland Etruria and Latium. These "ex-voto" have a common trait: the elongated deformation of the body, in some cases almost a geometric shape, in contraposition to the head, which is always executed in the round. Within central Italy's elongated ex-votos, our statue has two traits that sets it apart from the others: the lack of attributes such as specific type of clothing or gestures which define its social or religious status, and the vigorous plastic appearance of the body, well perceived even with its elongated deformation. Due to the lack of information on the archeological context of its place of origin, dating must be exclusively based on stylistic criteria. The care given to the somatic traits appear to underline the intention of reproducing well-defined individual characteristics which emphasize the inflow of 3$^{rd}$-2$^{nd}$ Century BC Greek portraiture. In addition, the rather unconventional hairstyle which echoes late-Hellenistic terracotta heads links the statue to the same chronological period. On said basis, the bronze may be dated back to the 3$^{rd}$ Century BC.

Along the walls, urns on the theme of the *deceased husband who appears to the wife to take her with him in the world of the dead*. Others believe it is a mythic event linked to Erifile who, corrupted by the necklace of Armonia donated to her by Tersandro, obliges her husband to take part at the war in which he will die.


## ROOM XVI

In the center, a mosaic coming from Segalari (Castagneto Carducci, Livorno).


## ALABASTER ECOMUSEUM

This room displays a synthesis of the cases' bas-relief subjects exhibited in the rooms on the second floor according to the "philological" criterion previously mentioned. It is a selection of alabaster urns of exceptional quality, the "soft stone" which in Etruscan times most likely was extracted from the quarries of Ulignano and Gesseri, near Volterra. Alabaster is still today the trademark of high quality Volterra crafts, even though the stone is extracted in quarries other than those used by the Etruscans. Beginning in the first decade of the 3rd Century until the first Imperial Age, alabaster was used only for funerary purposes and for urns in particular. Other types of objects like vessels or statuettes are extremely rare and only few exemplars exist. From a chemical point of view, alabaster is a calcium phosphate formed during the crystallization process in those faults still containing marine water residues. It is thus a "soft" stone well suited for virtuosic working but, unlike marble, it is not suited for the outdoors. The urns were located in chamber tombs (as the reconstructed tomb in **ROOM XXXVIII** on the third floor) destined to host the whole extended family and were constantly accompanied by a series of common objects that symbolically aided the deceased in the afterlife.

The almost one thousand urns discovered (of which over 600 are preserved at the Museo Guarnacci) come from a well-defined context, the town of Volterra and its territory, and they all belong to a precise period, a three-hundred year time span between the 3rd and the 1st Century BC.

Aside from the rare terracotta production of which there are only few isolated exemplars, the urn production in Volterra is equally distributed between the ones made of limestone (locally incorrectly called "tufa") and those made of alabaster. The latter material – without doubt more precious – was used beginning in the last decades of the 3rd Century for superior quality exemplars of larger dimensions (60/100 cm in length) which were sculpted in detail, painted, and at times gilded. It is clear they were destined for a wealthier clientele.

The urns were made in artisan's shops similar to the ones found nowadays in Volterra where a maestro worked together with assistants. At the high peak of urn production (2nd Cent. BC) there were no more than three shops, each producing 5/6 urns per year. The existence of apprenticeships – and the maestro's sons surely worked with the father – justifies the persistence of technologies, iconographies, models, and compositional schemes which are the base of the shop's tradition. Most likely – but with no certain information since there are no epigraphs to confirm it – the artisans who worked in Volterra had Greek origins and schooling, which explains the presence of urns of exceptional quality. The lack of the maker's signature prevents the exact placing of the urns within the social context. It is very likely that in a strong aristocratic context such as that of Volterra, the sculptors were considered at the lowest levels, even though perhaps not really identified with slaves.

The superior quality urn cases in this room (the original lid is not identifiable) are a synthesis of their former layout on this floor of the Museum:

RIGHT SIDE:

no. 292 Death of Anfiarao and battle between Centaurs and Lapiths (composition cartoon)

no. 291 Battle between Lapiths (peoples of Tessaglia) and Centaurs (Fig. 49)

no. 319 Hunt of the wild bore Calidonio

no. 270 Centaurs with women on their backs

no. 314 Appearance of the deceased husband to the wife

no. 215 Death of Mirtilo

LEFT SIDE:

no. 252 Abduction of Helen

no. 257 Abduction of Helen (Fig. 50)

no. 247 Telefo in the Greek battlefield

no. 356 Death of Atteone

no. 384 Recognition of Paride

no. 376 Killing of Troilo

Fig. 49. Urn case no. 291

Fig. 50. Urn case no. 257

## ROOM XVII

In the center of the room, a mosaic found in 1864 in the Church of San Francesco.

## ENTERING TO THE LEFT: WATER BEARERS FROM THE VOTIVE OFFERINGS OF DOCCIOLA (VOLTERRA)

The group, originally composed of four bronzes, was casually brought to light in 1971 during public works and restoration of the medieval fountain of Docciola. They were found by some workmen who handed them over to the Museo Guarnacci where they are now preserved. It is possible that some of the recuperated artifacts have been lost.

Water bearer inv. no. 1971/1. (h. cm. 20,8) **(Fig. 54)**.

Elongated laminar figure of a boy with a short skirt tied on the waist (*limus*) with his left hand holding an ovoid vase resting on his shoulder. The hand of the right arm, bent at the elbow, is resting on a side. Small roundish head, slightly bent to the right and with generic somatic traits. The locks of wavy

50

Tav. 51. Water carrier

Tav. 52. Water carrier

Tav. 53. Water carrier

Tav. 54. Water carrier

hair combed backwards and diverging on the forehead have been executed with thin engravings.

Water bearer inv. no. 1971/2 (h. cm. 12,9) **(Fig. 53)**
Male figure with short skirt tied on the waist (*limus*) represented as he is about to stand up under the weight of the ovoid vase resting on his left shoulder. The right arm is bent at the elbow and the hand is resting on a side. The left leg is in front, slightly bent at the knee. The other leg, which bears the weight, is bent with its foot on the side. Roundish face, slightly flattened out and with sketchy traits. Crown hairstyle with short bangs on the forehead.
The small votive offerings display a very important novelty represented by the water bearers, otherwise unknown in the vast Etruscan bronze context. Other exemplars of these figures, here executed both in the elongated way (1971/1) and with "normal" proportions (1971/2), are part of the Guarnacci collection (inv. no. 12/52, 76). They are ascribed to a local shop during the first half of the 3rd Century BC **(Fig. 51, 52)**.

The three showcases in the center of the room: red-figured vessels made in and around Volterra:

*KELEBAI (COLUMN KRATERS) MADE IN AND AROUND VOLTERRA*

The column kraters (kelebai) **(Fig. 55-58)** are the most representative vase nucleus ascribed to the Volterra shops produced in the second half of the 4th Century BC, perhaps even in the first decades of the 3rd Century BC.
These vases, originally intended to mix water and wine but commonly used for the deceased's ashes (funerary kraters) are characterized by the curvilinear shape of the neck, usually very elongated compared to the belly, and ending with a very thin brim.
They have been found in various necropolises of northern Etruria, particularly in Volterra and its territory, a fact which has led experts to believe this type of vase was produced in the shops of Volterra.
As in other Etruscan centers of the north, the beginning of production is associated to the inflow of Faliscan red-figured vessels to which also themes and motifs are linked.
However, due to the tight relationship with the vessels produced in Chiusi the

question concerning the birth of a local production in Volterra is still much debated. In fact, earlier experts dealing with this subject believed that artists from Chiusi moved to Volterra where they began the production of these red-figured vessels.


*Krater MG 42* (**Fig. 55**)

Krater MG 42 belongs to the Guarnacci collection and was executed by one of the most important red-figure decorators of Volterra, namely the painter commonly defined "**Pittore di Hesione**". The name derives from a lovely kelebe coming from the necropolis of Palazzone in Perugia representing Heracles saving the nymph Hesione by killing the sea dragon. Two sides of the krater from Volterra depict a naked female riding a dolphin with a long wind-swept ribbon (tenia). The fragment of krater MG 97 (**ROOM XXXVII**) featuring the head of a veiled woman wielding a thyrsus is also ascribed to the same Pittore di Hesione.

A characteristic of this Maestro is the chiaroscuro technique rendered with outlinings and particular details for the rendering of the eye, in addition to the custom of placing a decorative element in front of the faces. Another important exemplar executed by Pittore di Hesione is the kelebe in the tomb of Portone 1970/7 exhibited in **ROOM XXXVII** (330-310 BC).


*Krater MG 49* (**Fig. 56**)

On side A, the representation of a centaur moving towards the left and holding with one hand a tree stick and a pillow with the other.

On side B, two figures facing each other: a naked boy on the right holds a strigil (a spoon used to clean oneself from the oils the athletes used before competitions) in front of a woman with a horn-shaped vase in one hand and an unguentary vase in the other.

This work has been attributed to **Pittore Senese** (according to others, to the shop of Pittore di Milano) and stands apart from the rest of the production ascribed to Chiusi and Volterra. In fact, many decorative elements of the main figures and of the accessories regularly echo the decorations of the Chiusi vessels. This fact and the rather short and stocky shape of the vase with a short and large neck, very similar to the kraters from Vulci from which

Tav. 56. Kelebe no. 49

Tav. 55. Kelebe no. 42

Tav. 58. Kelebe no. 44

Tav. 57. Kelebe no. 43

Volterra's kelebai originate, leads to ascribe this exemplar to a first production phase of the Volterra group. It may be dated between 350 and 330 BC.

In the center of the room: **Calyx krater MG 89 from Montebradoni** (Volterra) **(Fig. 59).** One of the most important northern Etruria's red-figured vessel artifacts, this krater was discovered in 1870 in a tomb of the necropolis of Badia-Montebradoni, near Le Balze. It is an isolated exemplar as no other calyx krater has been found in Volterra and Chiusi's figurative production during the Hellenistic period. The

Fig. 59. Krater from Montebradoni

representation features a series of characters, deities and heroes, in a continuous sequence without an apparent logic relationship, almost displaying a "gallery" of figures merely for decorative purpose. Even though the scene has been interpreted in many different ways, it offers no concrete results. It is possible that the decorator had no experience of narrative composition and thus, inspired by complex Greek mythological representations perhaps taken from an early 4th Century BC "cartoon", he reinterpreted it without truly understanding the meaning.

The result is a work of art of figurative prominence executed by a painter with high calligraphic skills who has been conventionally named **Maestro di Montebradoni.**

Two additional kraters (MG 102 and 103) of the Guarnacci Etruscan Museum have been ascribed to the same Maestro from Volterra – and not from Chiusi as it was initially believed. The use of a functional line that emphasizes the volume and the lightness of the robes covering the figures with wind-swept draperies and the characteristic rendering of the hair with undulating lines forming small arches around the heads are typical of this Maestro's style (last decades of the 4th Cent. BC).

**The mirrors**

Typical female object, the Etruscan mirror is one of the most emblematic product of Etruscan bronze shops from the 6$^{th}$ to the 2$^{nd}$ Century BC.

The Etruscan mirrors display common and constant characteristics through-out their production time: the round shape of the disc with a smooth convex reflecting side (the mirror), at times silver-plated to make it shinier, and with a concave front side with finely engraved decorations (rarely in relief).

The earliest exemplars (6$^{th}$-end 4$^{th}$ Cent. BC) have a tang on the lower part of the disc to be inserted into a bone or ivory handle, which was made sepa-rately and fixed to the disc with a trapezoidal plaque. The handle of Hellenistic exemplars (end 4$^{th}$-2$^{nd}$ Cent. BC) is fused together with the disc and the lower part ends with a stylized ram.

The most common subjects for the decoration of the mirrors' reverse side are linked to Greek mythology, heroes (the preferred ones are Zeus' sons, the Dioscuri), deities assimilated to those of the Etruscan pantheon (especially Aplu-Apollo, Zeus-Tinia, Turan-Afrodite), and minor Etruscan deities whose names are often identified by the inscription on the mirror.

The most active mirror production center of southern Etruria was Vulci. It is difficult to locate the production area of the many documented mirrors in northern Etruria especially from the 4$^{th}$ and following centuries, mainly be-cause of the standardization of the products based on models and cartoons found in the many production centers. It is likely that there were one or more shops in Volterra and Chiusi.

## ROOM XVIII

SHOWCASE 1 (head jewelry)

*Crown.* Coming from Volterra. Purchased in 1867. Inv. MG 5. Length cm 28,50 **(Fig. 60)**.

A symmetric bundle of laurel leaves are applied on top of a narrow lamina band with semicircular tongue extremities shaped like an embossed wanderoo

head. The central part has a bulla surrounded by laurel leaves.
End 4<sup>th</sup>-3<sup>rd</sup> Century BC.

*Crown.* Volterra, necropolis of Portone. Purchased in 1861. Inv. MG 4.
Length cm 28.50 (**Fig. 60**).
A symmetric bundle of thin olive leaves with stamped veins are applied on a
narrow lamina band with semicircular tongue extremities. The lateral tongues
with a loop hole are decorated with stamped palm trees on volutes bordered
with small olive leaves.
End 4<sup>th</sup>-3<sup>rd</sup> Century BC.

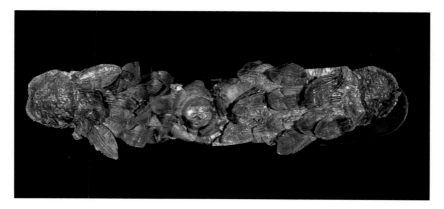

Fig. 60. Gold funerary crowns

*Pyramid earring* (**Fig. 61**). From Volterra, necropolis of Portone, 1873-1874 excavations in Lecceto. Volterra Inv. 94. Height cm 4.3; disc diameter cm 1.3.

It is made of two parts: the higher one is made of a circular disc with lamina bent on the edges, embossed decoration with concentric hollow circles and dome relief in the center. There is a hole at the apex with a suspension hook made of a thin gold string. An upside-down pyramid hangs from the lower part of the disc, smooth on the out-side and hollow on the inside.

Between the 3$^{rd}$ and 2$^{nd}$ Century BC, these disc earrings with upside-down pyramid were common in Etruscan culture, coinciding with the height of alabaster urn production in Volterra: in fact, the females sculpted on the covers often wear this type of ear-ring. This model reproduces in a very simplified way the more elabo-rate ones of the Magna Grecia, espe-cially Taranto, common in the 5$^{th}$ and 4$^{th}$ Centuries BC. The earring was found in a chamber tomb with many funerary urns and burial goods dating over a time span between the 3$^{rd}$ and 1$^{st}$ Century BC.

Fig. 61. Pyramid-shaped earring

*Earring with Negro head* (**Fig. 62**). From Volterra. Inv MG. 222. Height cm 1.85.

Gold earring with spiral string ring with end button and amber Negro head set in a choker with pearl rims and small cup with filigreed strigoses in which the neck rests. The head is covered by a cap covered with granulations on top of which there is a rod ring hook on which the end globe of the ring is placed. Aside from some details, our inedited earring is close to Etrurian exemplars, in particular those from Bettona and Orvieto. Around the 3$^{rd}$ Century BC.

*Earring with lion protome*
An original piece of M. Guarnacci's mid-18ᵗʰ Century private collection. From Volterra inv. MG. 37. Diameter cm 1.80.

The half ring bow is made of a spiral gold tube which enlarges at one end and ends with a lion protome with finely shaped snout and mane. The hollow eyes contained a vitreous paste or a semi-precious material. Under the protome, a small choker with rims in relief and filigreed strigoses at the base.
It is a very common earring in Etruria and Magna Grecia, especially in the area of Taranto. This type of jewelry is also found on Etruscan mirror shrines portraying female heads.
End 4ᵗʰ Century BC.

Fig. 62. Gold earring with Negro head

## ROOM XIX

The cover of urn no. 613, better known as **"urna degli sposi"** (spouses' urn) **(Fig. 63)** holds a prominent position in this room. It is a very suggestive monument: together with the elongated bronze statuette (the so-called **"Ombra della Sera") (Fig. 48)** in ROOM XV, it is one of the symbols of the Guarnacci Etruscan Museum. It is a lid with two figures representing a married couple reclining at a banquet. The execution of the faces is made with apparent realism and the details of the clothing exhibits an extremely high technical virtuosity enabled by the material used, terracotta, which is well suited to the quick strokes that allow a careful execution of even the smallest detail.

The dating of this unique piece made in Volterra is both uncertain and contested. Recently, it has been suggested to take into consideration a series of historical and ideological elements. Many details clearly indicate that this funerary monument does not belong to a standardized production but specifically made to order by a customer who wished to be represented in the "ancient" way. The iconographic rediscovery of the couple at a banquet, which symbolically represents the family bond (examples thereof found in the earliest urn production period of end 3$^{rd}$ –early 2$^{nd}$ Cent. BC), and the use of the same material as in the first urn production phase, terracotta, point at the customer's evident retrospective will. This coincides with the flourishing revival of earlier traditions which characterized Volterra's aristocracy after the siege of Silla, which led to the destruction of the town and to the loss of its autonomy.

Fig. 63. Terracotta lid ("urna degli sposi")

# ROOM XX

The four shelves in this room display a remarkable collection of unpainted and partially painted vessels for daily use. This is the typical "poor" furnishings of many burials of the 2nd-1st Century BC. The placing strictly follows their typology. Along the walls, there are Greek-Italic and Roman amphorae, at times found in 3rd-1st Century BC burials.

Walking into the room, on the left corner there is a clay vessel with ducts perhaps used in the making of wine.


# ROOM XXI

The showcase in the center of the room and the whole right wall display a collection of **materials purchased in 1884 at Serre di Rapolano, near Chiusi.** The idea of the museum coordinator of those days, Niccolò Maffei, was to provide the exhibit with important Etruscan materials such as the *buccheri* which, for some reason, were not found in the excavations of the town's necropolises.

In fact, the Chiusi collection is abundant with this particular type of vessels, typical of Archaic Etruria, but totally absent in Volterra, coinciding with the 6th-5th Century "gap" which marks the town.

In the showcase in the center of the room, *upper shelf*: **black figure pottery** (6th Cent. BC); *middle shelf*: **kylikes, kantharoi and skyphoi with red figures** (5th Cent. BC); *lower shelf*: vessels of different Hellenistic periods (4th-1st Cent. BC) and two **bell cinerary urns**, typical of the area of Chiusi. One of them bears a painted inscription: *hasti petrus*.

On the right side of the room in *showcases 1-4*: **buccheri produced in Chiusi.** On the lower shelf of showcase 1: **Corinthian and Etruscan-Corinthian pottery** of the 7th-6th Century BC.

The "bucchero pesante" (heavy, thick-walled vessel made of bucchero) is typical of Chiusi's production and widespread in a large part of central hinterland and southern Etruria. Compared to earlier productions (the light, thin-walled "bucchero sottile" of the 7th Cent.) of this particular type of vessels marked by the shiny black color of the outside and more opaque in the inside, the "bucchero pesante" is characterized by thicker walls and heavier ornamental elements, from which the name is derived.

The most frequently used decorative elements are human and animal heads, executed in the round or with a mould.

Typical "bucchero pesante" objects of the Chiusi production are the *foculi* (three exemplars in the lower shelf of showcase 4), food trays with miniature pottery ware and eating accessories, still made of bucchero. The *foculi* have a symbolic function and exclusively a funerary use.

Showcase under the right window: three large "bucchero pesante" amphorae. The middle one is decorated "with cylinders".

In showcases 5-6, **painted black vessels**.


ROOM XXII


Showcase 1. Terracotta materials and vessels. Noteworthy are no. **14**, a **support or decorative part of a kline with winged Sphinx** in bas-relief (**Fig. 64**); no. **13**, a **fragment of terracotta urn perhaps of male figure**; no. **15-25 candlestick** pieces, one painted black; no. **27-37 vessels from Arezzo** and late-Italic of Imperial Age. Among these, an exemplar of the production of sealed north-Italic land by *L. Sarius Surus*. No. **38-47 "silver-plated" pottery** probably produced in Volsinii (end 4th Cent. BC). A nucleus of said vases was also part of the burial treasures of tomb no. **61/7** of Badia (**ROOM XXVII, third floor**). No. **41-44** small plates with base and painted decoration belonging to the group conventionally defined **"Genucilia"**, of southern Etruscan production.

Showcase 2. **1-25 statuettes** for funerary purposes. They are all made of clay except for exemplars **8-9-10** in tufa and no. **7** in alabaster. It is important to note that alabaster was used only in funerary artifacts and not for everyday objects. Typologically speaking, the woman and child no. **22** may be linked to the marble statue exhibited in **ROOM XXXV on the third floor** (the so-called "Kourotrophos Maffei"). It was found during the hypogeum in the necropolis of Portone excavated in 1873 by Annibale Cinci.

Under the statuettes, on two boards (A and B) there are dice, stone draughts, and knucklebones. They were used for "board" games perhaps similar to today's checkers and backgammon.

On the lower shelf of the showcase, a collection of Imperial Age terracotta lamps. Many of them bear the trademark: no. **1, 10, 27, 31, 32**: FORTIS;

no. 3: SAECUL; no. 4:
L. FABRIC(IUS)
MAS(CULUS); no. 5:
FELIX; no. 6: VIBIANI;
no. 17: APRIO; no. 18:
C(AIUS)   IUN(IUS)
BIT(INIUS);   no.   2:
Q.G.C.;   no.   30:
C(AIUS) DESSI(US);
no. 34: ATIMETI; no.
44: STROBIL(US).
Showcases 3-4. **Painted
black vessels produced
in Volterra**
Showcase 5. **Iron** (lower
shelf) and **bronze** (upper
shelf) **candlesticks**.

Fig. 64

Showcase 6. **Etruscan inscription**. The **three lead sheets** (no. 1, 2, 3) coming from the tomb discovered in 1755 in the necropolis of Ulimeto are worth
mentioning. They have been interpreted as *tabellae defixionis* containing **mag-
ic curse formulae** and the names of many Etruscan families from Volterra.
The text, among the longest ones known to us, is very unclear. On the lower
shelf, a round memorial stone made of local sandstone found in the necropolis of Ripaie. It is the oldest inscription located in Volterra and dated around
600 BC. It bears the following words: *mi velthurus kana tusnutinas* [I (am) the
tomb of Velthur Tusnutina]. Next is an achromatic light-colored clay
cinerary vase with an inscription on the rim: *larza:aule:arnvalisa* [larza aule
(son) of arnth]. It belongs to the Hellenistic period (2$^{nd}$-1$^{st}$ Cent. BC). The
word *larza* is short for the given name *larth*.
Worth noticing on the middle shelf to the right of the showcase a series of
false inscriptions (no. **16-18**) made in the 18$^{th}$ Century on original black
painted fragments. Some of them, believed to be authentic, were published by
Florentine expert Anton Francesco Gori (Museum Etruscum, Florence,
1737).

# ROOM XXIII

The furniture and the disposition of the objects inside the showcases have been intentionally left as Niccolò Maffei had placed them in 1877. In this way, they offer an important flash-back on the conditions and museum criteria of the past century. This room exhibits a heterogeneous amount of bronze materials and a remarkable numismatic collection. The objects are placed by typology and do not follow a chronological order, exception made for Imperial Age coins.

Showcase 1. Upper shelf, large laminated bronze vases. In the middle, collection of fibulas from the first Iron Age (9$^{th}$ Cent. BC) to the 1$^{st}$ Century BC, and buckles (no. 183-196) from the 8$^{th}$-7$^{th}$ Century BC.

Showcase 2. Upper shelf, bronze vases of large dimensions. Object no. 364, with its unusual shape, was perhaps used in the making of wine.

In the middle, armilla (bracelets); horse bits with small horse decorations: no. 538, 540, 42, 957, small wheels and phalera. All these objects belong to the first Iron Age/Orientalizing period (8$^{th}$-7$^{th}$ Cent. BC); no. 514-525 chirurgical tools most likely of Imperial Age. Following, many small bronze objects (styluses, amulets, rings, small bullas) and three lamps (of Imperial Age). The two spurs (no. 537) are of Longobard origin.

Showcase 3. Upper shelf: bronze vessels.

In the middle: remarkably interesting are some parts of the kline, the dining couch on which the Etruscans rested during the banquets: no. 683 and 683/1 are the "*fulcra*", decorated with mule and horse heads and human figures (Erote and bearded satyr). No. 688, 682, 685, 620, 614, 617, 618, 683/2, 683/3 are the kline's additional parts or decorative elements.

No. 681 is the lower part of a large bronze krater. On the right side of the showcase, no. 627-653 are part of key locks (no. 651).

On the lower shelf, no. 962 simpulum (ladle or drinking cup), no. 691 bronze laminated disc with dented rim; no. 955 candlestick shaft; no. 712, 713 kist base with lion feet; above to the left no. 656-675 vase bases, no. 604-609 bronze nail heads; no. 919 series of bronze nails.

Showcases 5-6. Bronze vessels. Showcase 6 displays a copious collection of decorated vase handles.

Showcase 7. No. 194 large feline bronze paw. It must have belonged to a rather large statue like that of the famous Chimera of Arezzo (Archeological Museum of Florence).

In the middle of the showcase no. **808-813, 823-825** lance arrowheads (no. **807**). On the back of the showcase, a series of acorn-missile bullets to be used with a slingshot.

Showcase 8. High above, bronze vessels. In the middle, a large collection of strigils, the tool used by athletes to eliminate fat from their bodies and perfumed oils they put on before exercising. Some exemplars have trademarks on the handles (no. **9, 17a, 53**).


## THE NUMISMATIC COLLECTION

The collection was put together with purchases, especially made in Rome, and private donations. The interest of Antonio Ormanni, the Guarnacci Etruscan Museum's first director (1786-1801) was essential as he contributed in a fundamental way to the collection of Greek, Roman and Etruscan coins.

Please notice that the collection of coins coming from the mint of Volterra during the 3$^{rd}$ Century is exhibited in showcase 1 of ROOM XXXIV on the next floor.

The collection of Etruscan coins displayed according to the mint of origin in the stand of showcase 7 is extremely interesting **(Fig. 65-70)**.

In the lower part of the showcase, 18$^{th}$-Century false coins. The Roman coins of Republican Age in the stands of showcases 1-6 and 8 follow in alphabetical order according to the family name. The earliest exemplars are the coins of the *Afrania, Pinaria* and *Saufeia* families dated 200 BC. The Imperial and Byzantine coins follow a chronological order.

The showcase under the window to the left displays Hellenistic coins (especially Magna Grecia ones) and others coming from the Roman provinces.

In the showcase on the right there are exemplars of *aes rude* and *aes signatum* and a small collection of Roman and Italic *aes grave*.

Tav. 65. Silver coin from Populonia

Tav. 66. Silver coin with male head

Tav. 68. Coins from Populonia

Tav. 67. Silver coin from Pisa

Tav. 69. Casted Etruscan coins

Tav. 70. Casted Etruscan coins

## ROOM XXIV

Showcase 1

**Ivory and bone.** Most of the objects here exposed are decorative elements or everyday tools.

Noteworthy, on the panel above to the left: reconstruction of a curious tool found in the Cinci excavation yard in the necropolis of Portone, 1860. Apparently, the shape recalls a small umbrella.

No. **25, 26** and **30** are probably spindles used for spinning.

No. **18** flabellum handle (fan).

The four panels above to the right display styluses to carve waxed slabs and pin needles. The head of no. 110 is shaped like a hand with two (or perhaps three) straight fingers. No. 80 is a spatula most likely used in cosmetics. Under: no. 62 applied bone decorations with a protome of Gorgone and no. 63 decorative element with hollow human face . They come from the necropolis of Portone (1860 excavation). No. 144 frame pieces that perhaps decorated a small wooden box. No. 54: nine ring exemplars, one of which decorated with thin carved lines.

No. 133-143 ivory and bone game dice; no. 15/1 bone armilla with decorations of quadrigas.

No. 1, 2, 5, 6, 9-12 mirror handles; the inside metal tang of no. 14/1 is still visible.

No. 3, 4, 7, 8, 13 truncated-conical bone elements, perhaps mirror handles. To the left, no. 69 small cylindrical bone pyxis with lid. It comes from a tomb of Portone excavated in 1859, as well as comb no. 64.


Showcase 2

**Bronze statuettes**

The collection has a remarkable number of exemplars, even though in rare cases the place of origin is known. For chronological and documentary purposes, some of the statuettes of the Guarnacci collection have been moved to other rooms: exemplars of the Archaic period in showcase 1 of ROOM II, ground floor, and Hellenistic ones in ROOM XXXIII on the third floor.

The placement of the objects on the left and in the middle follow a chronological order while the others a typological one. Noteworthy are: figures of offerers armed with a sword (second half of the 7th Cent. BC), figures of offerers armed with a lance (second half of the 7th Cent. BC), kouroi with arms out in front (6th Cent. BC.), kouroi with arms resting along the body (6th Cent. BC), female and male figures of offerers (5th Cent. BC) **(Fig. 71-74)**.

The man on horse (no. 1911/2) **(Fig. 75)** comes from Casale Marittimo and originally was part of the decoration of the handles of a large bronze krater produced in Vulci. A large series of bronze statuettes belongs of course to the Hellenistic period (3rd-1st Cent. BC) **(Fig. 82, 83)**. Other important exemplars are located in ROOM XXXIII on the third floor. The central part of the showcase displays the bronze statuettes of deities like Heracles no. **99 (Fig. 76), 52, 9/52, 50, 8152, 9/1, 75**, Iside no. **70, 71, 79**, and Hermes **(72, 7/21, 74)**. The right side of the showcase is devoted to small animal figures (bovidae, birds, felines, and horses) at times part of decorations applied to different kinds of objects **(Fig. 80, 81)**.

Tav. 71. Bronze statuette of male offerer        Tav. 72. Bronze statuette of female offerer

Fig. 73. Male bronze statuette        Fig. 74. Bronze statuette of discobolus

Showcase 3

**Bronze mirrors**

The same may be said even for this part of the Guarnacci collection: many exemplars have been moved and arranged in ROOM XXXIII on the third floor, in the section devoted to Hellenistic period bronzes.

Nonetheless, this showcase has important and noteworthy exemplars. Among them stands out no. **921** which represents two dancing female figures facing each other. It belongs to the first half of the 5$^{th}$ Century BC and unfortunately its place of origin is unknown. From a chronological point of view, it is the Museum's oldest bronze mirror exemplar.

In the same section there are exemplars of different types of mirrors compared to the canonic ones with tang or fused handle. Among these, some have a rectangular shape, common during late-Hellenistic and Roman time.

Fig. 75. Decorative element of krater handle of Vulci from Casale Marittimo

Fig. 76. Bronze statuette of Heracles

Fig. 77. Bronze statuette of Lare

Fig. 78. Bronze statuette of male offerer

Fig. 80. Bronze statuette of feline

Fig. 79. Bronze statuette of male offerer

Fig. 81. Bronze statuette of hare

Fig. 82. Hellenistic bronze statuettes

Fig. 83. Bronze statuette of female offerer

# ROOM XXV
## Jewelry and jems

As foreseeable, there are very few objects from earlier times (Orientalizing and Archaic) while the goldsmith art of the Hellenistic and Roman periods are well documented.

If we exclude the exceptional documentary exemplars coming from nearby Gesseri di Berignone **(ROOM II, ground floor)**, there is no other jewelry dating back to the 7th Century BC, which was the wealthiest and richest time in the history of Etruria.

*Ear jewelry*

Two earrings belonging to the 6th Century (no. **90**) are shaped like a "box" **(Fig. 84)** and were common in Archaic Etruria. They come from the tomb of Portone excavated in 1873 by Cinci.

Beginning in the 4th Century, documentation increases.

The rather large earrings with empty ring and filigreed decorations date back to the 4th Century. On two occasions (no. **64/10** of Badia, ROOM XXXVII showcase 3, and the tomb of Portone) **(Fig. 88, 89)** it has been documented that the earrings were located inside a red-figure krater produced in Volterra (kelebe) in mid-4th Century BC **(Fig. 85, 87)**.

Exemplars no. **27-33, 216** and **218** are displayed in the showcase.

There are many small earrings with the hook shaped like a cornucopia (no. **39, 40**), at times ending with the protome of a lion (no. **32**) or tiger (no. **36, 38**). More common are those with spiral string (no. **41, 42, 233**) or with a simple gold string, a copious number exhibited here (ex. no. **265-270**).

Fig. 84. "Box-shaped" gold earrings

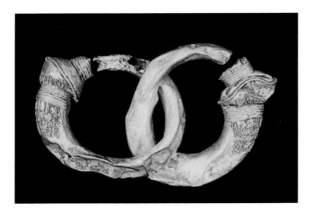

Fig. 85. Gold earrings with empty loop

Fig. 86. Earrings with laminated plaquettes

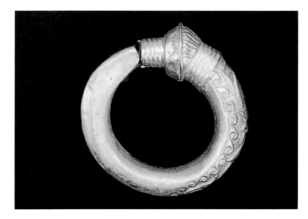

Fig. 87. Gold earring with empty loop

Fig. 88. Tomb 64/10 (necropolis of Portone)

Fig. 89. Tomb 64/10 (necropolis of Portone)

Fig. 90. Gold earring with pelta

*Hand jewelry*

The collection of hand rings is remarkable, often purchased from antique dealers.

The earliest exemplars are no. **106, 255** and date back to the end of the 4ᵗʰ Century. They are the so-called "eye" type rings made of a decorated oval shaped collet often filigreed or granulated, in the middle of which there was a semiprecious stone, which in our exemplars has been lost **(Fig. 91, 92)**.

 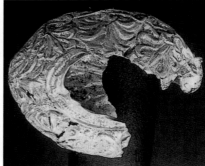

Fig. 91. "Eye-shaped" ring          Fig. 92. Gold ring

The other gold rings have a more generic chronological placement (from the 3ʳᵈ Cent. BC to the 1ˢᵗ Cent. AD), among which noteworthy are: no. **116** with semi-precious stone with a Negro head carving; no. **115, 130, 257** with smooth and small semiprecious stone; no. **213, 105** with collet without stone.

no. **224, 137, 228, 188** are with empty rod.

no. **133 (Fig. 94)** has a unique shape with collet made of two clasping hands and no. **256** with collet shaped like a sitting dog. Following are no. **135** made of a gold string with an interwoven ring collet; no. **132** with emerald collet; no. **127** with round collet with carving of a bearded head, typical Hellenistic tradition; no. **134** with spheroidal collet; no. **136** semicircular in shape with filigreed decoration.

Rings no. **119, 117, 118** are silver with vitreous paste collet; no. **125** is gold with turquoise; no. **110** is gold with naked standing figure resting on a tree trunk, discovered during the 1873 excavations in the necropolis of Portone. The collet of no. **104** displays a standing female figure; no. **109** has a carved vitreous paste; no. **97, 98** are rings made of one single piece of oriental agate; no. **19** ring of gold string of the "serpent" kind.

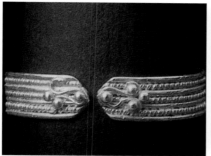

Fig. 93. Gold ring

Fig. 94. Gold ring

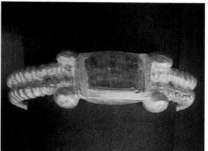

Fig. 95. Gold ring

Fig. 96. Gold ring

Fig. 97. Gold ring

*Neck jewelry*

no. 226 necklace fragments; no. 2, 7 chain; no. 15 arbitrary reconstruction of a necklace fragment with materials found during the 1875 excavations in the necropolis of Portone.

*Miscellaneous materials*

no. 22 silver needle (from the necropolis of Portone, 1873 excavation); no. 16 gold pin with head made of a two-faced female protome (from the necropolis of Portone, 1785 excavation).

Series of small round gold laminas with embossed star-shaped motif, perhaps decorative element for textile or clothing. They come from the 1873 excavations in Portone.

In the small nucleus of gold filaments (no. 1) there was a small ring made of massive gold with emerald collet no. 131 and both were located inside urn no. 452 featuring a voyage to the underworld on a chariot (**ROOM VIII, ground floor**), discovered during the 1860 excavations in the necropolis of Portone.

*The gems*

During the last decades of the 6$^{th}$ Century until the Hellenistic period, in Etruria there was a widespread use of rings with a rotating scarab-shaped gem, often made of carnelian or onyx, with finely carved figures echoing Greek mythology. The rotating scarab was fixed on a gold or silver string or rod and was in fact a signet ring.

Among the exemplars, worth mentioning are no. 51 and 152 with Egyptian hieroglyphics, and no. 144 and 143 with Arab inscriptions. These are typical 1700s collectibles rich in heterogeneous materials.

It is interesting to note that the gold collets with semiprecious stones and inscriptions of no. 155, 156, 158, 143, 166, 134, 165, 167, 168, 141, 157, 168, 142 are modern (1700s-1800s). no. 171-179 are Imperial Age cameos, some of them (no. 173, 171) of doubtful authenticity.

Fig. 98. Carnelian scarab

Fig. 99. Carnelian scarab

Fig. 100. Carnelian scarab

Fig. 101. Carnelian scarab

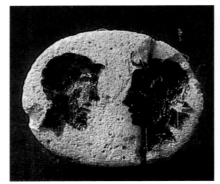 

Fig. 102. Carnelian scarab          Fig. 103. Seal

Fig. 104. Seal

## ROOM XXVI
### Roman Volterra

Roman Volterra is eloquently described by the grand theater of Vallebuona, a building of imposing proportions built by the will of two members of the Etruscan family Ceicna/Caecina who obtained the consulate in Rome during Augustan Age.

In this room (right wall when entering, above) there is a reconstruction of the theater's memorial epigraph where A. Caecina Severus and A. Caecina Largus are mentioned, the two patrons who between 1 BC and 25 AD provided the financial means and workmen for its construction.

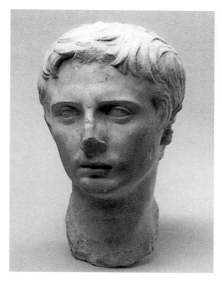

Fig. 105. Head of Augustus

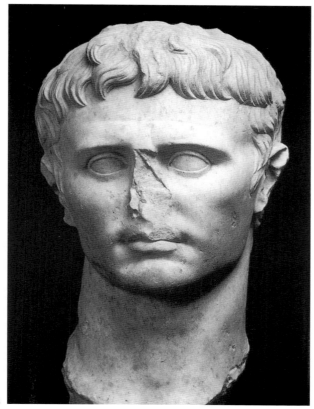

Fig. 106. Head of Augustus

A series of marble heads are located under the epigraph, the three middle ones come from the theater: two heads of Augustus (Fig. 105, 106) and one of his wife Livia Drusilla (Fig. 107). Between the heads there is a two-headed Bacchus and Ariadne (coming from Rome) and at the two extremities, images most likely portraying citizens.

On the left wall, there are large fragments of a polychromatic mosaic coming from the Roman villa discovered in 1969 outside Porta Fiorentina (Fig. 108). The floor dates back to the $1^{st}$-$2^{nd}$ Century AD.

In the room, there is also a reconstruction of a "cappuccina" tomb (Fig. 109) with tile cover ($3^{rd}$ Cent. AD) coming from the necropolis of Ripaie (1969 excavation). On the right wall, a series of small marble and tufa urns (Fig. 110). In the showcase, Imperial Age burial furnishings.

In the center of the room, a sundial belonging to the four magistrates of the Poena family and an altar-shaped urn (Fig. 111) (Augustan Age) coming from the 1739 excavation at the necropolis of Portone, originally bearing a painted inscription – today lost – recalling a person of the *gens* Caecina Caesaula.

Fig. 107. Head
of Livia Drusilla

Fig. 108. Polychrome mosaic

On the back, a recent restoration intervention: the so-called **Prete Marzio** (Fig. 112).

This toga-clad statue is known at least from the early 1600s when it was clearly identified (*Statua Martii Romani*) on the historical-archeological map enclosed in the work *Ethruscarum antiquitatum fragmenta* by Curzio Inghirami

Fig. 109. "Cappuccina" tomb

Fig. 110. Marble urn case

(Frankfurt, 1637). In another book, the same author describes it as a *statua al naturale et alla romana, togata e senza testa* (real size Roman style statue, toga-clad and without head).

The traditional shape in which it has been preserved until today is the result of a series of 1800s restorations by hand of Antonio Faltoni of Volterra who, by wish of the town's Gonfalonier Giulio Maffei, carried out the sizing of a monumental head for the truncated body – surely not pertinent – and the su-

Fig. 111. Urn shaped like an altar

perposition of two "shoulders" made from small marble blocks coming from the Cathedral of Volterra.

The final result is that of a *pastiche* typical of last century's style and which was visible until 1922 from the terrace overlooking the fountain of Santo Stefano, in the place formerly called Prato Marzio, from where the name of the statue is derived.

Today's restoration has allowed to remove the non-pertinent additions and to fill in some original lacunae, thus returning the statue to its original shape.

The main part of the Prete Marzio is composed of the trunk of a toga-clad statue in standing position with arms bent forward, wearing a *toga fusa* with wide *sinus* on the knee, *balteus* and *umbo*, a type of robe which by wish of Augustus substituted the Republican Age *toga restricta*. Near the left foot there is a *capsa* in which the *rotuli* were placed, the symbols of a person's political power.

The sketchy execution of the back part of the drapes indicates the monument was to be placed in a niche and thus would have been visible only from the front.

The head, which on inauguration day was placed on the bust, belongs to the Guarnacci Etruscan Museum collection and surely is not pertinent. However, the type of marble, the execution and the state of preservation are very similar to the toga-clad statue. The head therefore provides a vision of the monument's original shape – even though only for purely didactic and explanatory purposes – which was built in such a way as to allow the placing of a different head according to the historical moment.

Fig. 112. Toga-clad Roman (known as "Prete Marzio")

## HELLENISM

With the Hellenistic period (end 4$^{th}$-1$^{st}$ Cent. BC) the town experiences a time of high artistic, cultural and economic prosperity. The abundance of artifacts (sculptures, vessels, bronzes, coins) coming from the necropolises of Badia, Portone, and Ulimeto, which have been studied in-depth since the beginning of the 1700s, and the development and spreading of the high quality craft production confirm Volterra's importance and prosperity. A wide geographic area is linked to the town, both culturally and economically, including the whole Cecina valley and its coast, and the valleys of Era and Elsa.

The origin of such prosperity is linked to the persistent and largely productive farming tradition, which guaranteed to the town and its territory a constant prosperity, and to the far-seeing good political relationship to Rome, with which a peaceful alliance treaty was stipulated around mid-3$^{rd}$ Century BC. These two factors, the friendship with Rome and the stable farming economy, are confirmed by Volterra's supply of wheat and wood to the Roman fleet during the Second Punic War (205 BC).

The construction of an over 7 km long imposing city wall (4$^{th}$ Cent. BC) turned Volterra into a strong and well-defended citadel against Celtic and Ligurian invasions from the North. This is why the Romans favored the town and used it as the base for their operations against the incursions of these peoples. Volterra's geographic location, which had limited its growth during the Etruscan "mercantile" expansion, now became a determining factor and allowed the town to emerge in a time when other southern Etruscan towns began their decline, destined to be absorbed by the Roman expansion.

**ROOMS XXVII-XXXII** and **XXXVIII** still display cinerary urns. While in the past they were organized according to mid-1900s erudite criteria, they now reflect an arrangement corresponding to new research guidelines.
**ROOMS XXVII-XXVIII** exhibit a series of tomb complexes discovered in recent time, in particular at the necropolis of Badia, which allow an immediate understanding of the chronological evolution of cinerary urns and the association of objects found inside the tomb.

A section of **ROOM XXIX** hosts two important urns of the Tomb of the Calisna Sepu of Monteriggioni that substantiate the spreading use of these cinerary urns in the area under Velathri; the rest of the room exhibits an allusive reconstruction of a tufa and alabaster crafts shop.

The high quality monuments exposed in **ROOM XXX** follow a well-defined chronological order (end 3$^{rd}$-1$^{st}$ Cent. BC) and have been ascribed to the work of artisans, most likely coming from Greece, who established in Volterra sculpting schools and marked their works with unique "trademarks".

**ROOM XXXI** primarily deals with the theme of the clients' ideology, while **ROOMS XXXII** and **XXXII bis** host some monuments illustrating the problematic of portraiture. This part of the itinerary ends with **ROOM XXXVIII** and the reconstruction of an intact tomb discovered in 1970 at the necropolis of Portone.


## ROOM XXVII


Urn with double sloping tufa cover no. **45**: decoration on three sides of the case with rampant marine dragons on the front and darting dolphins on stylized curly waves on the sides (second half of 4$^{th}$ Cent. BC).

In the center of the room: urns no. **5, 193** (cover only).

no. **5** displays a reclining female figure slightly turned to the left; on the case, two felines attack a deer (**Fig. 113**). The representation of the half-recumbent deceased is part of the earliest urn production phase with human illustrations (second half of the 4$^{th}$ Cent. BC). no. **193** (**Fig. 114**): female figure on the cover resting on the left side and wearing only a robe, with her breasts showing (end 4$^{th}$ Cent. BC).

Entering, on the left wall: tomb **61/7** of Badia.

Cinerary urn no. **677** (**Fig. 116**) with semi-reclined deceased with bare chest and patera in his right hand. Parallelepiped case on a lion-foot base. On the front, traces of a painted scene of the voyage to the underworld set within a hollow rectangular frame.

Burial treasure (**Fig. 115**): set of silver-plated vessels (situla, strainer, pan, oinochoe, 3 olpai and 2 thymiateria), 2 umbelicated pateras, 4 small plates and a small cup painted black (beginning 3$^{rd}$ Cent. BC).

Only the tufa cover of Tomb **61/5** is preserved and features a half-reclined deceased with bare chest **(Fig. 117)**. Burial treasure: a skyphos of the Ferrara set T. 585, an olpe and a black painted kylix, a krater fragment with traces of reddish paint, a crown with gold leaves broken into numerous fragments which thus was not possible to reassemble (beginning 3<sup>rd</sup> Cent. BC).

Fig. 113. Urn no. 5

## ROOM XXVIII

ENTERING, TO THE LEFT:

**Room tomb 60/D** of Badia; five intact tufa urns were found in the tomb together with various fragments of alabaster urns and a copious burial treasure exhibited in the showcase in the center of the room and composed of vessels, bronzes, and coins. Three of the urns are decorated with bas-reliefs: alabaster urn no. **651** portrays a scene from the *Killing of Mirtilo*; urn no. **652**, tufa with alabaster cover, depicts *Eteocle and Polinice preparing for the battle*.

Fig. 114. Female lid no. 193

Fig. 115. Burial treasure of Tomb 61/7 from Badia

Fig. 116. Cinerary urn no. 677

Fig. 117. Tomb 61/5 from Badia

Tufa urn no. 654 features *Telefo in the Greek battlefield*. The other urns, no. 653, 655, have uncarved cases.

The discovery of coins in the urns located in this tomb is remarkably important and were presented as follows:

no. 653 sextans of the Velathri series and Roman semis of the sextans series. no. 655 quadrans and semis of the sextans series. no. 654 semis of the uncial series.

The coins displayed in the first shelf of the showcase have made it possible to date the urns in which they were found between 200 and 160 BC.

Burial treasure: Showcase 1. Upper shelf from left to right. Set of mixing vessels (three vases) painted brown (olpai, oinochoai, a small askos, a small plate and a cup); set of black painted vases made in "Malacena" among which are a small plate with inscription carved on the external side of the dish: *Cavina*; the same inscription is found on a red painted bowl on the lower shelf. In the same section, two bronze mirrors, spindle-shaped unguentaries, three large askói and a clay krater originally painted and used as a cinerary urn. Even though the excavation took place in recent times (1960), no documentation has been made about the layout of the objects inside the chamber tomb, exception made for the coins.

**Tomb XII** of **Portone** (1970 excavation).

Tufa urn no. **690** with smooth case and recumbent female on the cover was found on the bench on the back; on the bench to the right, tufa urn no. **691** with reclining female figure on the cover and a scene of doubtful meaning portraying the *journey to the underworld of a warrior on a quadriga*.

Showcase 2. Burial treasure: two non-depurated clay vases, two oinochoai with rolled spout, a small vase and an askós painted shiny black, two bronze mirrors one of which with tang handle, two bronze gilded rings, a kyathos, a spear and iron nail fragments, a set of astragals (mid-3$^{rd}$ Cent. BC).

Showcase 3

**Tomb 61/15** of **Badia.**

Female burial inside urn no. **678** with case decorated with bas-relieves depicting a scene of the *deceased husband appearing to the wife to take her with him in the afterlife* (for the interpretation of this subject refer to p. 47). Burial treasure: unpainted or partially painted vessels, two small plates painted brown, a kylix fragment painted shiny black, two hemispherical cups, a fragment of a round bronze mirror, and a Roman as coin of the sextans series. This coin is dated 189-158 BC and thus sets the *terminus post quem* for the dating of the tomb which should then belong to the last decades of the 2$^{nd}$ Century BC.


# ROOM XXIX


During the Hellenistic period, cinerary stone urns were used as tombs in the entire geographic area under Velathri. It is unknown whether the urns were produced in loco by wandering artisans in the Etruscan settlements in the valleys of Era, Elsa, and Cecina or if they were made by shops located in town. Most likely during the first production phase the urns were not exported from Volterra. This is the case of the hypogeum of Monterrigioni from where the two urns located in the left corner of the room come (**Fig. 118, 119**). The tomb, discovered on December 7, 1893, contained 105 burials, 36 of which were stone urns. According to the customs of the time, the tomb was dismembered and the pieces were divided between the museums of Volterra, Florence, and Berlin.

Urn no. **632**: on the cover, male figure with bare chest and patera. On the case, the scene of *Achilles with the head of Troilo and Aiace* laterally delimitated by two fluted columns.

On the right side, winged female demon. On the left side, Charon. On the upper fascia of the front of the case there is an inscription which continues on the base of the back part of the cover: *Larq: Calisna: Cursnialisa: Sepu:* (third quarter of the 3$^{rd}$ Cent. BC).

Urn no. **631**: on the cover, a recumbent infant figure, naked and deformed, holds an apple in the left hand and has a round object placed in front, perhaps a flat bread. The original polychromy is clearly visible: the body is painted red while hair and eyes are black.

Parallelepiped case on four feet with decorated red and black geometric elements (end 3$^{rd}$ Cent. BC). This is the only funerary monument of the area of Volterra portraying an infant.


## THE SHOPS

Even though over 1,000 cinerary urns were found in the necropolises of Volterra and its countryside, there is no trace of the shops where they were produced.

It is unknown whether the shops were located near the burial sites or – more likely – in town.

In-depth technical studies bearing in mind objective information have allowed to carry out an indicative reconstruction of a tufa and alabaster shop in

Fig. 118. Urn no. 632

Fig. 119. Urn no. 631

Volterra active between the end of the 2$^{nd}$ and the 1$^{st}$ Century BC during the "mass" production of urns.

The utensils have been lent by artisans from Volterra who still today carry out this 2,000 year old tradition.


## ROOM XXX


From the second half of the 3$^{rd}$ Century BC, the urn production in Volterra is marked by a superior quality in parallel with mass production destined to moderately wealthy clients. This higher quality production was intended thus for the aristocratic, erudite and wealthier clientele.

Based on more recent studies, which have contributed to the characterization of shops and individual artisans, this room displays urns of exceptional craftsmanship, the products of meticulous sculptors believed to have had Greek schooling.

Noteworthy is the fact that this precious production was always made of alabaster, the calcareous gypsum typical of the area of Volterra, very similar to marble but softer: an ideal stone for the detailed virtuosity of the decorations executed by these master artisans.

Urn no. **228 (Fig. 120, 121).** On the cover, reclining crowned male figure. On the plinth, the inscription: *l. precu. larisal.* [laris precu (son) of laris]. The case features *Recognition of Paride.*

Fig. 120. Alabaster urn no. 228

Fig. 121. Male portrait

Unfortunately presenting many lacunae, this composition was executed during the mature period of the Greek artisan conventionally known as **Maestro di Mirtilo** (around 160 BC). The name comes from the theme of one of his loveliest and best preserved works: urn no. 93484 exhibited at the Archeological Museum of Florence and depicting the scene of the *Killing of Mirtilo*.

Typical of this sculptor is the rendering of the characters with extremely high reliefs, almost "in the round", and the rigor used in the composition canonically based on four characters gravitating on extremely oblique axes. The dramatic force of the movement combined with the baroque virtuosity in the rendering of draperies and details hint at Maestro di Mirtilo's strong personality and to his Greek-island, perhaps Rhodes, schooling. Urn cases no. 259 with a scene of the *Gauls raiding the temples* (Fig. 122) and no. 338 (Fig. 123), traditionally interpreted as *Menelao threatens Helen to death*.

These are two important exemplars of the production of a shop conventionally defined as *of the rosettes and small palms* due to the "signature motif" found on the many works of this prolific atelier in Volterra. In fact, the upper cornices of the urns are decorated with an elegant vegetation motif made of rosettes alternated with small palms.

Fig. 122. Urn no. 259

Fig. 123. Urn no. 338

From a stylistic point of view, it appears this production is linked to the teachings of Maestro di Mirtilo, yet with very different connotations. For example, the geometric rigor of the Maestro's typical composition is not reproduced; instead, they favor a crowd of characters depicted on the front of the case, which is no longer laterally delimitated by fluted columns or pilasters. In this case, the human figure takes over the decorative elements used to delineate space. The working of the volume of the body and the rendering of the draperies still follow a baroque virtuosity in style, yet they are extremely refined. Both works are dated around mid-3$^{rd}$ Century BC.

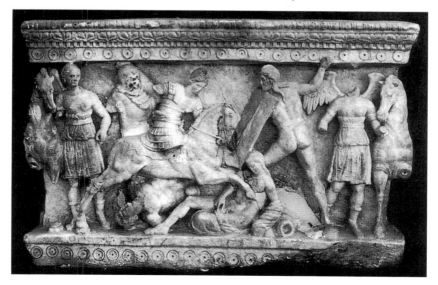

Fig. 124. Urn case no. 427

Fig. 125. Urn case no. 245

Urn cases no. 427 with scene of *Battles against the Gauls* (Fig. 124) and no. 245 with *Telefo in the Greek battlefield* (Fig. 125).

Even in this case, the urns belong to a well-identified atelier with a "signature motif" consisting in *small pateras*. It is the decoration of the upper frame of the lower base, probably executed with a specific drill, which apparently depicts umbilicated pateras viewed from the bottom. Not only do the scenes lack the dramatic force which characterizes the productions by Maestro di Mirtilo and his followers in favor of more composite rhythms, but also the baroque virtuosity in the rendering of the draperies is absent.

However, the volume of the bodies is still strongly marked: the sculptors follow the classicism of neo-Attic schooling. Second half of the 2nd Century BC.

## ROOM XXXI

The dislocation of cinerary urns in the Guarnacci collection has already somehow introduced the problems related to said subject matter suggesting a rigid separation between themes linked to the voyage to the underworld and episodes of Greek mythology. The family's choice for one theme rather than another to be represented on the urn reflects an attitude which allows us, *a posteriori*, to characterize an entire social reality. Greek literature, especially tragedy, was part of the Hellenistic "literate" class from where the choice of identifying the deceased with a myth of noble origins and thus underlining the knowledge of said episode. In general, it is believed that these mythological episodes underwent a complex cultural routing before becoming part of the common themes used by the Etruscans from Volterra. The many representations, for example, came from cartoons that reproduced famous works by artists who collaborated to the exaltation of Pergamo's dynasty, and who used the myths for allegoric and celebrative purposes. It is thus plausible to believe that those master artisans from Greece introduced the Greek myth in Volterra, and thus were the *trait-d'union* between Hellenistic culture and local clients. On the other hand, the typical Etruscan beliefs, in which the funerary dimension is evident, reflect a lesser "intellectual" relationship with death. This is clearly visible in their emphasis on the deceased's institutional function while alive, expressed in the careful attention to the ceremonial procession which accompanies him to the afterlife: musical band, insigne of his power, quadriga, etc.

It is too simple and substantially arbitrary to identify the social condition of the deceased based on the subject featured on the urn which was chosen by the family. However, in the least it has a double connotation: a nucleus of aristocratic families with a strong Greek culture imitated by a rather large number of wealthy followers compared to a middle-class composed of artisans and small land owners still strongly linked to ancient traditions.

ROOM XXXI displays various urn cases with the most common mythological subjects and just as many depicting the themes of the voyage and farewell. Worthy of mention is urn no. 350 (Fig. 130) featuring an exclusively Etruscan myth, the monster rising from the puteal.

From the left, entering: urn no. 226: *Recognition of Paride* (Fig. 133); urn no. 169: *Magistrate on a quadriga*; urn no. 135: *Voyage to the underworld on a chariot* (Fig. 127); urn no. 355: *Oedipus and the sphinx* (Fig. 126); urn no. 280: *Ulysses and the Mermaids*; urn no. 114: *Voyage to the underworld on horse*; urn no. 290: *Hero combating with a plough* (Fig. 131); no. 46: *Darting dolphins*; urn no. 371: *Assault to the walls of Thebes*; urn no. 62: *Scilla* (Fig. 129); urn no. 511: *Telefo in the Greek battlefield* (Fig. 132); urn no. 87: *Farewell scene* (Fig. 128); urn no. 350: *Monster rising from the puteal*.

Fig. 126. Urn case no. 355

Fig. 127. Urn case no. 135

Fig. 128. Urn case no. 87

Fig. 129. Urn case no. 62

Fig. 130. Urn case no. 350

Fig. 131. Urn case no. 290

Fig. 132. Urn case no. 511

Fig. 133. Urn case no. 226

## ROOMS XXXII and XXXII bis

It has already been mentioned that when observing the over 600 urn covers one has the impression, as suggestive as it is fallacious, of having in front the faces of the people of Volterra about 2,000 years ago. The real portrait, the so-called physiognomic one based on the union of the true reproduction of the somatic traits of an individual and his psychological characterization, is not found in the urn covers from Volterra, if not in exceptional cases.

The production time and modality favor more a reproduction in series of pre-set "types" (the boy with the bulla, the man with the patera, the young lady with the mirror, the matron with the fan, etc.).

Most of these typologies come from a prototype the artisan then modified with some individual traits or with the addition of an attribute that best explained the deceased's social condition.

In this room and the following one there are several examples of particularly important iconographic typologies: no. **483, 181, 118** and **291** are examples of "heroic" portraiture. The deceased is represented wearing only a robe, with a bare chest and the face echoes portraits of Macedonian and Oriental dynasties of the first Hellenistic period. Urn case no. **350 (Fig. 134-136)**. As opposed to this portraiture tendency which may be defined as "literate", during the first decades of the 2$^{nd}$ Century Volterra developed a more simplified and readily accepted typology, an example thereof are covers no. **572, 414 (Fig. 137)**. In this case, the model comes from Rome where neo-Attic sculptors worked. The forerunner of Volterra's representations was the famous peperino head coming from the Scipioni sepulcher (now exhibited at the Musei Vaticani), erroneously ascribed to the tragic poet Ennio.

Fig. 134. Urn lid no. 483

Fig. 135. Urn lid no. 181

Fig. 136. Urn lid no. 291

Fig. 137. Urn lid no. 414

Two pairs of covers are displayed in **ROOM XXXII bis** which illustrate how the accentuated characterization of the somatic traits is still not sufficient to define these faces as true portraits.

Before the affirmation of the veiled type, in late 2nd Century a new model proliferated characterized by a very short body and a marked interest for the face, which was still based on late-Hellenistic Greek portraits.

The two covers on the right side of **ROOM XXXII bis**, no. 174 (**Fig. 138**) and no. 346 (**Fig. 139**), belong to a series conventionally classified as

"Luvisu 1" and date back to 140-110 BC; the other pair (no. **335, 339**) (**Fig. 140**) belongs to the same period, or slightly more recent ("Gruppo Luvisu 2"), end of the 2nd-beginning of the 1st Century BC.

## ROOM XXXIII
**Bronze works**

Right side: *the mirrors*. Typical female objects emphasizing the technical skills of Etruscan artisans in

Fig. 138. Male portrait urn no. 174

Fig. 139. Male portrait urn no. 346

Fig. 140. Male portrait urn no. 335

the founding, working, and decoration of the metal, already praised by Greek and Latin writers. Showcases 1 and 2 display a remarkable number belonging to the Hellenistic period (4$^{th}$-2$^{nd}$ Cent. BC). For the most part, the exemplars are of the common type with handle founded together with the round piece, convex on the mirror side and concave on the external one where there are fine decorations carved with a graver. The theme is generally limited to isolated characters, in particular winged female demons (Lase) or pairs (Dioscuri, Castore and Polluce sons of Zeus). Rarely the scenes have a wider breadth, with deities taken from Greek mythology. These handcrafted products most likely come from Greek-Hellenistic prototypes imitated by Etruscan artisans with an incorrect understanding of the models as they were more concerned with the filling of the available round space. The exemplars displayed at the Guarnacci Etruscan Museum are not of the best quality.

From right to left:
*Persefone and three Goddesses* no. 922 (**Sketch 2**)
*Lasa naked and winged* no. 903
*Satiro and Baccante* no. 920
*Persefone and Dioscuri* no. 916
*Naked Dioscuri* no. 912
*Sileno and Lasa* no. 917 (**Sketch 5**)
*Lasa naked, winged, and with Phrygian cap* no. 896 (**Sketch 6**)
*Lasa naked, winged, with Phrygian cap, and alabastron in the hand* n. 887
*Mercury's head* no. 911 (**Sketch 1**)
*Mercury with Caduceo Venere and a third figure* no. 900
*Persefone and two figures* no. 919
*Castore and Polluce* no. 905 (**Sketch 3**)
*Lasa naked, winged, and with Phrygian cap* no. 895
*Unidentified scene* no. 925 (**Sketch 4**).


To the left (showcases 10 - 1) *Plastic arts*.
Already in Augustan time, the *tyrrhena sygilla*, the small Etruscan bronze statuettes, enriched the treasures of the wealthiest Roman families.
Originally, the statuettes were primarily used for religious purposes: they were votive offerings in sanctuaries in exchange of requests or blessings received.

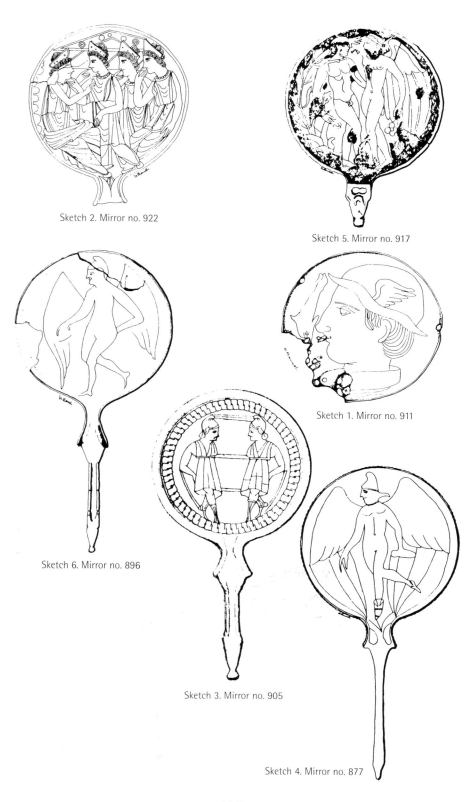

Sketch 2. Mirror no. 922

Sketch 5. Mirror no. 917

Sketch 1. Mirror no. 911

Sketch 6. Mirror no. 896

Sketch 3. Mirror no. 905

Sketch 4. Mirror no. 877

Showcase 10: no. **82, 86.** Male figures (one of which with many lacunae) wearing a robe and with a bare chest. Stylistically speaking, they echo classic Greek statues, particularly Policleto and his famous "spear-carrier". They date back to the end of the 4$^{th}$ Century.

Showcase 9: no. **84.** Female figure of an offerer with tunic and robe. In her left hand, an unidentifiable round object. Dated 2$^{nd}$ Century BC.

Showcase 8: no. **184, 32, 44, 39, 38, 43, 42.** Laminated statuettes of offerers wearing a tunic and robe, very rough execution; the details are only sketched. Dated 3$^{rd}$-2$^{nd}$ Centuries BC.

Showcase 4: no. **36, 20/32, 35.** Male figure of an offerer with patera in the left hand.

Showcase 3: no. **90/1.** Handle of a pan with female figure with crossed legs.

Showcase 2: handle with winged female figure holding a torch in her right hand.

Showcase 1: krater handles with bearded heads of Sileno **(Fig. 142)**.

Fig. 141. Handle of pan                    Fig. 142. Handles of a krater

Showcase 1

*Velathri coins*

The economic prosperity in the Hellenistic period is confirmed by the existence of a mint producing founded bronze coins following the Roman *libra*
weight system. The dating of three sets of coins from Volterra is controversial
(displayed in showcase 1). The first studies dealing with *aes grave* theme suggested a dating around 300 and 268 BC, and then more specifically between
271 and 268 BC. Recently, it has been suggested the coins from Volterra
were in use in the years following the Second Punic War (218-202 BC).
The numismatic finds discovered in the tombs in and around Volterra where
the coins from the mint of Velathri were used, do not indicate a date antecedent the 3$^{rd}$ Century BC.
Three sets are preserved, two of which ("of the value" and "of the club") have
all marks of value from the *dupondius* to the *uncia*, according to a duodecimal
weight system. Of the third set ("set of the dolphin") there is only the higher
marks of value: *dupondius, as and semis.*
Showcase 1 from right to left: *set of the value.* F/ two-faced beardless head with
cap (*culsans?*). B/ *Velathri* legend and marks of value. Average weight of the as
gr. 143.69.
*Set of the dolphin.* F/ two-faced beardless head with pointy cap. B/ *Velathri* legend, dolphin and marks of value. Average weight of the as gr. 144.41.
*Set of the club.* F/ head like the preceding one. B/ *Velathri* legend, club and value marks. Average weight of the as gr. 157.66.


Showcases 2 and 3

*The bronze vessels*

In his work *Dipnosophistae* ("Dissertations at a banquet") Ateneo di Naukratis,
a 3$^{rd}$ Century AD grammarian and philosopher, uses an erudite poetic cita-
tion by Critias, a Greek tyrant of the 5$^{th}$ Century BC and a poet in his free
time, where he praises the gold cups and the domestic bronze vases displayed
in the Etruscan homes.
Showcase 2, from right to left. Olpe (pitcher to pour), pyxis (perhaps a cosmetics container) with silver damascene decoration, kyathos (ladle or drinking cup), tymiatherion (perfume burner), olpe with silver damascene decoration, alabastron (unguentary), small hemispherical cup, pan, olpe.

Showcase 3, from left to right: situla (bucket) (Fig. 141) on three feline feet base, large tray with decorated handles, situla with lid and removable handles, a small flask (container for perfumed oils) and four flasks' mouths, oval-shaped situla coming from Tomb XII of Portone.

## ROOM XXXV
### The tomb epitaphs

For the Etruscans, the location of the tomb is often identified by a symbol which in some cases may be considered an epitaph. In this room there are various types of tomb epitaphs of the Hellenistic period, among which stand out two female

Fig. 143. Funerary stele

marble statues both belonging to the Maffei family from Volterra, but at different times. Their importance relies on the fact that they are two rare exemplars of female marble statues used for funerary purposes, only five of which have been attested to in northern Etruria. The material used is Italic marble perhaps coming from the Apuane Alps: its use in Volterra is certainly linked to the fact that such monuments were made for the outdoors and thus the local stone (alabaster), highly susceptible to atmospheric agents, could not be used. The bas-relief of the small tufa cinerary urn (placed between the two windows) suggest the statues were used as funerary epitaphs.

Based on recent studies, the execution of these epitaphs echoing erudite models of Greek funerary statues of the second half of the 4th Century BC may be ascribed to workshops active in Pisa during the first half of the 3rd Century. From the left, entering: "panchino" stele with inscription: *mi: ma: velus: rutlnis: avlelsla* [I (funerary epitaph?) of Vel Rutlni (son of) Avle]. Next, "panchino" stele with inscription: *mi: ma: laris: suplu* [I (funerary epitaph?) of Laris Suplu] (Fig. 143).

*Fragment of female marble statue* (Fig. 144). The headless trunk of the body and a portion of the lower part of the body. The figure wears a tunic tied to the waist and a robe. The statue is believed to portray a woman in the moment of "anakalypsis", the typical gesture of moving the veil according to the matrimonial rite.

*Female marble statue* known as *"kourotrophos Maffei"* (**Fig. 144**). The statue is missing the head and the lower part of the legs. It represents a woman holding a baby. The right arm bears a carved Etruscan inscription: *mi: cana: larthias: zanl: velcinei: se [...] ce.* Even though with some difficulty, the text is rather clear: the statue declares to represent a woman named Larthi (*mi cana larqias* = I am the image of Larthi). Another woman whose aristocratic name (*Velchinei*) and part of her given name (*se(...)* perhaps *sethra*), dedicated it (*turce?*). The meaning of the word *zanl* is

Fig. 144. Kourotrophos Maffei

rather obscure, as it appears not to be aristocratic. According to a plausible reconstruction, the head located in showcase 1 next to the statue should belong to the same statue.

Showcase 2. Quadrangular tufa memorial stone. It bears a long inscription on the front and on the sides: *l: titesi: cale \si cina: cs: mes \tles huq: naper \lescam letem: qui arasa: qen \tmase: laei: tre \cs qenst: me \naqa.*

This artifact was discovered in 1855 in a hypogeum of Marmini (necropolis of Portone) and dates back to the end of the 4th Century. From a paleographic point of view, the inscription may be linked to the previously described *kourotrophos* of the Maffei family. Without doubt, the text is obscure and does not allow any kind of interpretation.

Between the two windows: tufa cinerary urn no. 667. On the cover, recumbent female with fan in her right hand. On the case, a scene in bas-relief of doubtful meaning, perhaps related to funerary games in honor of the deceased. The small urn is placed here because the gladiators' fight takes place in front of a funerary monument composed of a high base on which a statue is placed (in this case, a male), and thus similar in its function to the afore-mentioned female statues.

To the right: conical travertine memorial stone shaped like a small column, inserted in its base with an inscription. It comes from the necropolis of Casone, Malacena yard (Monteriggioni, Siena), 1844 excavation. It belongs to the Terrosi collection, part of which was joined to the Guarnacci Etruscan Museum. The inscription is difficult to decipher: *larqi sarzlx: lesunilance mucezi: cemarzleraczle*. The text is not comprehensible, exception made for the initial female name: Larthi.


## ROOM XXXVI
### This room is used only for temporary exhibits


## ROOM XXXVII

From mid-4$^{th}$ Century BC, Volterra had vessel shops that produced medium and large vases with red figures exported to most of central-northern Etruria and Corsica. The most typical shape is the column krater (or *kelébe*), a vase originally used to mix water and wine. Many Hellenistic tombs revealed *kelébai* which still contained the ashes of the deceased, thus confirming that they were not simply part of the burial treasures, but were also used as cinerary urns. The decoration of these kraters is rather unique and almost always char-acterized by a reticulated decoration with a small cross inside each lozenge painted on the long vase neck. The body is painted with frames delimitated by small palms inside which there are figures reproducing with unique liveliness the figurative motifs typical of Greek (especially the vessel maker Meidias), Italiot, and Faliscan vessels of the end of the 5$^{th}$ and 4$^{th}$ Centuries BC.

Dancing figures, centaurs, Pygmies fighting with cranes, winged demons, columns, male and female profiles are the most common motifs found on these vessels, which appear to totally lack famous mythological subjects.

If it is commonly accepted that these kraters have been produced in Volterra, the same may not be said for another set of Etruscan red-figured vases (show-case 2), which are part of a dispute between those who believe they were made in Chiusi and others who ascribe them to Volterra. It is more likely that the *kylikes* and the vases shaped like a duck (*askói*) were produced by vessel mak-ers from Chiusi, while the pitchers (*oinochóai*) with satyrs or maenads belong to local shops. In addition, the large *skyphoi* (large and deep bowl-shaped wine cups with small horizontal handles) were also painted black and decorated with swans with spread wings and belong to the latter group of vessel makers.

Showcase 1
Upper shelf.
Kelebe no. **44**
Side A: Satyr and Maenad dancing naked; in the middle, basin on a high base.
Side B: Menade and Sileno dancing naked.
Kelebe no. **40**
Side A: Tuscan column.
Side B: oval-shaped shield.
Kelebe no. **38**
Side A: left profile of male head.
Side B: left profile of male head.
Kelebe no. **30**
Sides A and B: two figures facing each other, the male on the right is naked and holds a tapeworm in his right hand; the female wears a long tunic.
Fragment of kelebe no. **97/A**. There is part of the neck and of the belly of the krater with female figure holding a thyrsus in her right hand.
Kelebe no. **46**
Sides A and B: two standing naked female figures facing each other, with the right hand resting on a hip and a *rhytón* in the left hand.
Kelebe no. **29 (Fig. 146)**
Side A: naked Pygmy moving to the left with a staff in his right hand and a

Fig. 145. Skyphos of the Gruppo Ferrara T 585

Fig. 146. Kelebe no. 29

round object in his left.

Side B: naked Pygmy with the left hand resting on the hip and an unidentifiable object in the right.

Kelebe no. 32

Side A: right profile of male head.

Side B: left profile of female head.

Kelebe no. 28

Side A: naked female figure moving to the left holding in her hands the limbs of an open robe.

Side B: representation of a Kelebe.

Kelebe no. 39

Sides A and B: left profile of male head.


Showcase 2

Lower shelf. Three black skyphoi of the "Gruppo Ferrara T. 585" with red swans with spread wings painted over and floral motifs (Fig. 145).

No. 84: oinochoe (wine pourer). On the neck, left profile of female head flanked by two rosettes.

No. 87: oinochoe. On the body, five human heads facing once to the left and once to the right: Satyr, three Maenads, boy. The faces are alternated by two stylized flowers and two thyrsuses (Fig. 148).

No. 96: stamnos (Fig. 149).

Fig. 147. Stamnos no. 96

Fig. 148. Red-figured oinochoe no. 87

Fig. 150. Askos no. 69

Side A and side B: two figures facing each other: on the left, female figure with alabastron (small ointment vase) in the left hand and staff in her right; on the right, male figure resting on a side.

Upper shelf

Kylix no. 102: in the inner circle, three poorly preserved figures, from left to right: bearded satyr with thyrsus in his left hand, another satyr facing the preceding one and then a naked Maenad.

Fig. 151. Tomb 64/4 (necropolis of Portone)

Kylix no. 103: in the central circle from left to right: naked figure presumably a male of whom only the legs and the pleated robe are visible, lower part of a naked warrior's body with lance and shield, and a naked woman resting on a small column.

no. 69 (Fig. 150): askós (duck-shaped vase) with red figures.

Showcase 3 to the left (upper and lower shelves)

Right side of the showcase. **Necropolis of Ripaie tomb A1** (1969 excavation) (end 3rd Cent. BC).

Lower shelf. **Tomb of the necropolis of Portone 64/4** (beginning 2nd Cent. BC) (Fig. 151).


## ROOM XXXVIII
Tomb XIII of Portone (Fig. 152)

This room is dedicated to the reconstruction of a tomb as it was discovered on July 11, 1970 in the necropolis of Portone.

The excavation was carried out by Enrico Fiumi, at the time director of the Museum, with the assistance of some volunteers in Marmini on the property owned by Pineschi.

From a down-sloping entrance hall (*dromos*) facing North, with an average width of 40 cm, one enters a quadrilateral chamber (m 4.20X4) with a bench along the sides on average 60 cm wide and 70 cm high, where the urns were placed. From the center of the chamber, the height to the ceiling is 2.60 m. The entrance hall was sealed by a stone slab which was found intact. The tomb had not been despoliated: only a large piece of stone had fallen from the vault of the ceiling and laid in the center of the chamber between the benches. Humidity and water dripping had severely corroded the only two alabaster urns which, together with three others made of local limestone ("tufa" from Pignano), were placed on the bench to the right and on the back where also burial treasures (vessels, bronze statuettes, coins) were located. Other pieces fell between the benches where fragments of a non-painted bell-shaped cinerary krater were found. A similar one still containing the ashes of the deceased was on the right bench near the first limestone urn.

The tomb thus contained at least seven burials, five inside urns and two in cinerary kraters, covering a time span of possibly 3 or 4 generations between

Fig. 152. Tomb XIII of Portone

the last decades of the 3$^{rd}$ Century BC and the first half of the 2$^{nd}$ Century (circa 230-140 BC).

The earliest burials may be identified with the second female urn on the right bench with smooth case, originally painted red, inside which two different gold earrings were found (one made with a simple gold string and the other shaped like a Mermaid playing a syrinx) in addition to a ring without collet.

The main burial, however, must be identified with the male urn placed in a prominent position on the back bench with a copious burial treasure composed of vessels (wine and water pourers, drinking cups, plates). These were part of the "eating set" for the banquet which symbolically allowed the deceased to continue in the afterlife with the same level of luxury and customs he was used to. The large iron candlestick, still in its original placing, is also part of the banqueting set.

Some of the vessels still had food leftovers (bones of small animals and birds) and two eggs, one still intact, found near the large wine amphora placed on the left bench. This was the deceased's meal for his farewell supper, which was held by the family in front of the tomb in concomitance to the burial.

# EXIT HALLWAY
## The architectonic terracotta

A series of research projects conducted from 1969 to 1971 on the highest part of the town (Castello), in an area which miraculously escaped the 1472 Florentine works for the construction of the fortress (now a penitentiary), has provided important information for the town's historical definition.

More specifically, it is certain that the acropolis was Velathri's religious center and seat of two temples, the foundations of which were made of local stone and are still visible in the lovely park of the Castle dedicated to Enrico Fiumi. As it was typical for Etruscan temples, the sidewalls were made of wood and finished with terracotta.

A significant selection of clay architectonic decorations (of the so-called temple A) is exhibited here. The figures' impressive lacunae make it difficult to interpret their relationship and consequently to offer a coherent explanation of the decorative cycle.

The reconstruction of a small frontispiece (showcase 1) to which five figures have been attributed (a reclining female figure, a squatting satyr, a female torso, and two virile torsos probably part of a fighting scene) is rather convincing.

From a stylistic point of view, Volterra's terracotta cycle offers suggestive comparisons with the Taranto relief made of soft stone dating back to the end of the 4th-beginning 3rd Century BC and with analogous Etruscan exemplars such as the figurative slabs of the Hellenistic settlement in Vetulonia.

Showcase 1

*Small frontispiece* (?). From left to right: 1) half-recumbent female figure wearing a chiton and revealing the right breast, a limb of the robe falling over the left shoulder; 2) frightened from the scene taking place on its left, a squatting wanderoo figure is about to retreat; 3) female torso with tunic revealing the left breast and robe over the right shoulder; 4) left profile of virile figure with robe over the right shoulder; 5) virile naked figure in a strong rotating movement.

Showcase 2

From right to left: 1) virile head; 2) virile head leaning to the right; the head was covered with an elm; 3) fragment of head with elm; 4) virile head, the hair is comb in the typical *anastolé* hairstyle; 5) virile head with elm; 6) Corinthian-style elm.

Showcase 3

From right to left: 1) male figure with tunic and robe; 2) boy figure; 3) female torso; 4) fragment of female figure; 5) fragment of female figure; 6) slab with remains of a relief pilaster; 7) slab fragment with remains of a composite capital; 8) slab fragments with remains of a foot.

Printed by Pacini Editore September 2004
presso le Industrie Grafiche della Pacini Editore S.p.A.
Via A. Gherardesca • 56121 Ospedaletto • Pisa
Telefono 050 313011 • Telefax 050 3130300
Internet: http://www.pacinionline.it